NONLINEAR TRANSFORMATIONS OF RANDOM PROCESSES

PRENTICE-HALL INTERNATIONAL SERIES IN APPLIED MATHEMATICS

DEUTSCH, *Nonlinear Transformations of Random Processes*
DRESHER, *Games of Strategy: Theory and Applications*
EDMUNDSON, ED., *Proceedings of the National Symposium on Machine Translation, 1961*
STANTON, *Numerical Methods for Science and Engineering*

PRENTICE-HALL, INC.
PRENTICE-HALL INTERNATIONAL, INC., UNITED KINGDOM AND EIRE
PRENTICE-HALL OF CANADA, LTD., CANADA
BERLINER UNION, WEST GERMANY AND AUSTRIA

NONLINEAR TRANSFORMATIONS OF RANDOM PROCESSES

RALPH DEUTSCH

Space Systems Division
Hughes Aircraft Company
Culver City, California

PRENTICE-HALL, INC.
Englewood Cliffs, N. J.
1962

PRENTICE-HALL INTERNATIONAL, INC.
London • Tokyo • Sydney • Paris

PRENTICE-HALL OF CANADA, LTD.

PRENTICE-HALL DE MEXICO, S.A.

Library of Congress Catalog Card No. 62-15078
Printed in the United States of America
62324—C

to

CHARLOTTE

LESLIE

BARBARA

PREFACE

The objective of this book is to provide a comprehensive background on nonlinear noise problems for practical applications in communication and control systems. The subject of nonlinear transformations of random processes can be studied either from the point of view of *pure* mathematics to gain appreciation of general theoretic principles or it can be studied from the point of view of applied problems motivated by models and requirements of physical systems. A mixture of these approaches was chosen for the exposition.

There is an infinite number of nonlinear transformations since, by definition, every transformation which is not linear is nonlinear. For this reason, it would be expecting too much if one hoped to find a universal analytical technique applicable to any arbitrary random process transformed by any arbitrary nonlinear device. Progress, albeit slow, is usually attained by the process of selecting specific classes of nonlinear characteristics which, when coupled with selected types of random processes, produce a combination which is amenable to analysis.

The topics chosen for exposition are representative of the comparatively few known techniques for studying nonlinear transformations of random processes. For some situations it is possible to formulate the complete statistics of the transformed process. For most situations, however, one must be content with obtaining the relations for output moments and the correlation function. Even when valid for rather general situations, the described methods have been illustrated with only a few examples. Solving specific problems with these techniques quite frequently leads to mathematical manipulative difficulties that can only be surmounted by either almost infinite patience or by resorting to numerical solutions. These difficulties have led to the common practice of illustrating new analytical methods with examples which have already been treated by other techniques. This practice accounts for the repetition of the same illustrative examples and alternate formulations of the same problem. Thus the number of solved problems does not tend to increase with the number of available techniques for treating nonlinear devices.

The book is intended as an extension to the subject of noise theory suitable for reference and practical application. Since no mathematical preliminaries are included, it is assumed that the reader is already grounded in the elements of statistics and probability as well as in the basics of *Noise Theory*.

The first five chapters present specific classes of nonlinear devices and random processes which in combination lead to *closed form* solutions for the statistical properties of the transformed process. Chapter 6 treats techniques based upon the use of series representations. Approximate solutions are obtained by using a variety of series expansions for the statistical frequency function, nonlinearity, and even the correlation function.

Chapter 7 contains one of the first general systematic approaches to the subject of nonlinear transformations of random processes. For a Markov process, with only minor restrictions, integral and differential equations are formulated which serve as the solution for the statistical properties of the transformed processes.

Sampling and quantizing of a random process is discussed in Chapter 8. An appendix, containing notes on the hypergeometric function, is included for reference because of the frequency with which this function occurs in the illustrative examples.

The book is an outgrowth of research sponsored by the Hughes Aircraft Company. Their support for the original investigations and for the preparation of the final manuscript is gratefully acknowledged. Acknowledgment is also due to the System Development Corporation for aid in writing a preliminary draft of this material for use in an internal course on Noise Theory.

RALPH DEUTSCH

Sherman Oaks, California
May, 1962

CONTENTS

ENVELOPES AND PRE-ENVELOPES

1.1 Notion of an Envelope, 1
1.2 Envelopes and Pre-Envelopes, 3
1.3 Correlation and Spectrum Relations for Envelope Functions, 5
1.4 Example of Envelope Calculations, 10

CHARACTERISTIC FUNCTION METHOD

2.1 General Remarks, 13
2.2 Characteristic Function Method, 13
2.3 Nonlinear Devices having Gaussian Inputs, 15
2.4 Examples, 21
2.5 Comments, 26

CORRELATION FUNCTION METHOD

3.1 Computation of Moments, 27
3.2 Envelope Detector, 28
3.3 Envelope Square Law Detector, 30
3.4 Logarithmic Transformation, 31
3.5 Random Telegraph Signals, 33
3.6 Quadratic Transformations of Non-Gaussian Processes, 35

MULTIPLICATION AND POWER LAW DEVICES

4.1 Remarks, 42
4.2 A Common Fallacy, 42
4.3 Output Moments of a Power Law Device, 44
4.4 Series Representation of a Random Process, 45
4.5 Squaring and Filtering, 47
4.6 Reduction to Differential Equation, 50
4.7 Solution using Cumulants, 51
4.8 Filtered Thermal Noise, 54
4.9 Product of Two Processes, 57

MODULATION AND DETECTION

5.1 Simple Detection Model, 62
5.2 Simple Detectors, 64
5.3 Detection of the Sum of Random Processes, 71

SERIES APPROXIMATIONS

6.1 General Analytical Techniques, 75
6.2 First Probability Frequency Functions, 76
6.3 Correlation Function Expansions, 82
6.4 Second-Order Frequency Function, 88
6.5 Wiener's Method, 94
6.6 Representation of Nonlinear Operators, 105
6.7 Representation of a Frequency Function by its Moments, 109

TECHNIQUES USING DIFFERENTIAL AND INTEGRAL EQUATIONS

7.1 General Remarks, 112
7.2 Integral Equation, 115
7.3 Partial Differential Equation, 118
7.4 Solution of the Reduced Equation, 119
7.5 Moments, 120
7.6 Examples, 121

SAMPLING AND QUANTIZING

8.1 Introduction, 125
8.2 Periodic Samples Random Process, 126
8.3 Sampling Theorem, 127
8.4 Signal Quantizing, 134

APPENDIX: NOTES ON HYPERGEOMETRIC FUNCTIONS, 139

REFERENCES, 147

INDEX, 155

1 ENVELOPES AND PRE-ENVELOPES

1.1 NOTION OF AN ENVELOPE

The notion of the *envelope* of a time series is usually an intuitive concept arising from elementary studies of signal modulation. In Figure 1-1, one

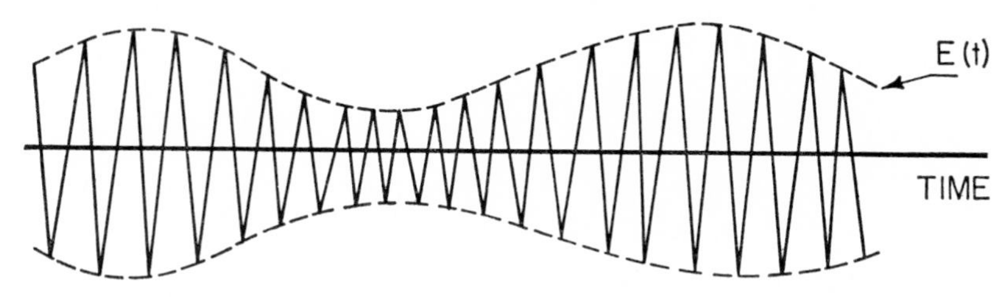

Figure 1-1. Modulated Voltage

easily *recognizes* the dotted lines to be the envelope of the modulated signal. If the signal is the result of modulation of one frequency by another, then we can write

$$E(t) = A(1 + m \cos \omega_m t) \cos \omega_0 t \tag{1-1}$$

where ω_0 denotes 2π times the carrier frequency f_0 and $\omega_m = 2\pi f_m$ corresponds to a frequency such that $\omega_0 \gg \omega_m$. Under these conditions the envelope function is defined to be $Am \cos \omega_m t$. The definition corresponds to what one would expect from an examination of Figure 1-1 and suffices for many discussions of modulation theory. However, more complicated signal forms are encountered when noise sources corrupt the signal. The simple concept of an envelope function is soon found to suffer from several defects.

Suppose we formally try to extend the simple definition of a signal envelope to a signal consisting of a wide sense stationary random process. Adopting the simple series representation of the process, for illustrative purposes, consider the signal

$$E(t) = \sum_{n=0}^{\infty} C_n \cos(\Omega_n t - \alpha_n). \tag{1-2}$$

α_n are random phase angles uniformly distributed in the range $(0, 2\pi)$ and $C_n^2/2$ is the signal power associated with frequency Ω_n. It is semantically convenient to call both $\Omega = 2\pi f$ and f the frequency.

Arbitrarily select some frequency ω_0 to be designated as the *midband* frequency. All other frequencies ω_n are then written as

$$\omega_n = \Omega_n - \omega_0. \tag{1-3}$$

Restrict the midband frequency choice so that $\omega_0 \gg \omega_n$. The $\{\omega_n\}$ will constitute a set of frequencies about ω_0 associated with random phase angles, α_n. Intuitively, we can see that the simple notion of an envelope function for the random process has little meaning unless the condition $\omega_0 \gg \omega_n$ can be satisfied for all the frequency components having significant power terms $C_n^2/2$.

Rewrite Eq. (1-2) in the equivalent form

$$\begin{aligned} E(t) &= \sum_n C_n \cos[(\omega_0 + \omega_n)t - \alpha_n] \\ &= E_c \cos \omega_0 t - E_c \sin \omega_0 t, \end{aligned} \tag{1-4}$$

$$E_c = \sum_n C_n \cos(\omega_n t - \alpha_n) \qquad E_s = \sum_n C_n \sin(\omega_n t - \alpha_n).$$

Eq. (1-4) can be put into the form of Eq. (1-1) by writing

$$E(t) = (E_c^2 + E_s^2)^{1/2} \cos(\omega_0 t + \phi). \tag{1-5}$$

By analogy with Eq. (1-1) the envelope function for the random process is defined as

$$V(t) = (E_c^2 + E_s^2)^{1/2}. \tag{1-6}$$

Several difficulties are immediately encountered in this *loose* definition of an envelope function. It is not at all clear that a different choice of the midband frequency $\omega_0^1 \neq \omega_0$ would lead to the same envelope function $V(t)$. If the condition $\omega_0 \gg \omega_n$ is not satisfied for all the significant terms $C_n^2/2$, what becomes of the intuitive notion of the envelope? Finally, because of the nonlinear relation in Eq. (1-6), it is a formidable task to compute $V(t)$ and is generally difficult, if not entirely impossible, to obtain the statistical characteristics of the random process $V(t)$.

1.2 ENVELOPES AND PRE-ENVELOPES

If $g(t)$ is a real-valued function on the interval $-\infty < t < \infty$, its Hilbert transform $\hat{g}(t)$ is defined as the principal value of the integral

(1-7) $$\hat{g}(t) = \frac{1}{\pi} \int_{-\infty}^{\infty} \frac{g(\sigma)}{t - \sigma} \, d\sigma.$$

Without further statement, all the functions considered in this chapter are assumed to possess Hilbert transforms. The following properties follow at once from the transform definition, [1].

(i) If $g(t) = \cos(\omega t + \phi)$, its Hilbert transform is $\hat{g}(t) = \sin(\omega t + \phi)$.
(ii) Under rather general conditions if $f = \hat{g}$, then $\hat{f} = -g$.
(iii) If $H(f) = \int_{-\infty}^{\infty} h(t) \exp\{-2\pi f t\} \, dt$ is the Fourier transform of $h(t)$, then the Fourier transform $Q(f)$ of the Hilbert transform $\hat{h}(t)$ is

$$Q(f) = \begin{cases} -iH(f); & f > 0 \\ \quad 0 \quad ; & f = 0 \\ +iH(f); & f < 0. \end{cases}$$

(iv) The convolution of two functions

$$w(t) = v(t) * u(t) = \int_{-\infty}^{\infty} v(\tau) u(t-\tau) \, d\tau$$

has the Hilbert transform

$$\hat{w}(t) = v(t) * u(t).$$

With these tools we are now in a position to present Dugundji's [2] approach to an unambiguous definition for the envelope of a real-time series. Although the use of Hilbert transforms to define envelopes had been used before, [3,4] Dugundji's work is the first extensive exposition on the subject.

Definition 1-1: If $h(t)$ is a real time series, its corresponding pre-envelope function $z(t)$ is defined as

(1-8) $$z(t) = h(t) + i\hat{h}(t).$$

Definition 1-2: The envelope of $h(t)$ is defined as the absolute value of the pre-envelope function $z(t)$.

The important point is to ascertain that these definitions reduce to the intuitive notion of an envelope for simple waveforms and still do not suffer the ambiguous defects of the *loose definition*. For example, consider the same time series $E(t)$ defined in Eq. (1-2). Its pre-envelope function is

(1-9) $$\begin{aligned} z(t) &= E(t) + i\hat{E}(t) \\ &= \sum_n C_n \cos(\omega_n t - \alpha_n) + i \sum_n C_n \sin(\omega_n t - \alpha_n). \end{aligned}$$

Choose an *arbitrary* frequency Ω and write

$$z(t) = \sum_n C_n \cos [(\omega_n - \Omega)t - \alpha_n + \Omega t] + i \sum_n C_n \sin [(\omega_n - \Omega)t - \alpha_n + \Omega t]. \tag{1-10}$$

This can be written as

$$\begin{aligned} z(t) &= [H_c \cos \Omega t - H_s \sin \Omega t] + i[H_s \cos \Omega t + H_c \sin \Omega t] \\ &= (H_c + iH_s)e^{i\Omega t}, \end{aligned} \tag{1-11}$$

where

$$\begin{aligned} H_c &= \sum_n C_n \cos [(\omega_n - \Omega)t - \alpha_n] \\ H_s &= \sum_n C_n \sin [\omega_n - \Omega)t - \alpha_n]. \end{aligned} \tag{1-12}$$

Using Definition 1-2, the desired envelope function is

$$V(t) = |z(t)|, = (H_c^2 + H_s^2)^{1/2}. \tag{1-13}$$

Notice that since $z(t)$ is independent of the arbitrary choice of the *midband* frequency Ω, $V(t)$ is also completely independent of this choice.

Although it has been shown that the definition of the envelope corresponds to the intuitive concept, the motivation and general applicability of the definition needs further amplification. We first note two properties of the pre-envelope function.

(a) Consider the Fourier transform of

$$z(t) = h(t) + i\hat{h}(t). \tag{1-14}$$

Applying property (iii), the result is

$$\begin{aligned} z(f) &= \mathfrak{F}[z(t)] \\ &= \begin{cases} 2H(f); & f > 0 \\ H(f); & f = 0 \\ 0 \;\;; & f < 0. \end{cases} \end{aligned} \tag{1-15}$$

(b) If $z(t)$ is a complex valued function whose Fourier transform, $Z(f)$, vanishes for all $f < 0$, then z is the pre-envelope of its real part. Thus, if $h = \mathcal{R}e(z)$, then $z = h + i\hat{h}$.

Property b can be demonstrated in the following manner. Define

$$H(f) = \begin{cases} \frac{1}{2}z^*(f) \;; & f > 0 \\ 0 \;\;\;\;; & f = 0 \\ \frac{1}{2}z(-f); & f < 0, \end{cases} \tag{1-16}$$

where the asterisk denotes the *complex conjugate,* and $H(f)$ is the Fourier transform of $h(t)$. That is,

$$h(t) = \int_{-\infty}^{\infty} H(f) \exp (2\pi i f t) \, df. \tag{1-17}$$

Employing the definition of Eq. (1-16), it follows that $h(t) = h^*(t)$, or that as defined, $h(t)$ is a real-valued function. Consider the pre-envelope function $y = h + i\hat{h}$ corresponding to $h(t)$. From *property a* it follows that the Fourier transform of $y(t)$ is $z(f)$, except possibly at the point $f = 0$. This implies that $y = z$ and establishes *property b*.

For most noise theory analyses of physical situations, the usual practice is to consider only positive frequencies in the frequency spectrum of a random time series. This is often accomplished in the mathematical analysis by doubling the positive frequency terms and neglecting the negative frequency terms. The common justifying argument is that the negative frequencies merely reflect the positive ones in complex conjugate form and, therefore, can be reflected into positive frequency terms. Notice that *property a* of the pre-envelope is nothing more than a statement that only positive frequency terms are considered with a doubling of coefficients.

1.3 CORRELATION AND SPECTRUM RELATIONS FOR ENVELOPE FUNCTIONS

In this section it is tacitly assumed that all the functions have the required properties that give meaning to all integrals and operations. These assumptions permit us to investigate some formal mathematical relations without considering all the exceptional cases for which the statements may fail to hold.

The important results developed in this section were obtained by Dugundji under the implied restriction that the random process was stationary and ergodic. Zakai has pointed out that these results remain true when the *time averages* employed by Dugundji are replaced by *ensemble averages*, regardless of ergodicity, the only requirement being that the process be wide sense stationary, [5].

Setting aside Zakai's generalization for the moment, let $x(t)$ and $y(t)$ be two wide sense stationary ergodic processes. Their cross-covariance function is defined as

$$R_{xy}(\sigma) = E\{x^*(t)\, y(t + \sigma)\} = R_{xy}{}^*(-\sigma). \tag{1-18}$$

Throughout this book, $E\{\cdot\}$ represents the expected value of the quantity within the braces.

The Fourier transform of R_{xy} is often called the *cross-power density spectrum function* and is denoted by the symbol $W_{xy}(f)$. Thus,

$$W_{xy}(f) = \int_{-\infty}^{\infty} R_{xy}(\sigma) \exp(-2\pi\, if\, \sigma)\, d\sigma. \tag{1-19}$$

We now derive some useful relations concerning the spectrum of the envelopes and pre-envelopes of real valued wide sense stationary ergodic random processes cognizant of the fact that it is known that the ergodic hypothesis can be omitted.

(c) The covariance function $R_{x\hat{x}} = \hat{R}_x$, where $\hat{R}_x$ is the Hilbert transform of $R_x = R_{xx}$.

By definition

$$R_{x\hat{x}} = E\{x^*(t)x(t+\sigma)\} = \frac{1}{\pi} E\left\{\int_{-\infty}^{\infty} \frac{x^*(t)\, x(\tau)}{t+\sigma-\tau}\, d\tau\right\}. \tag{1-20}$$

Assume that the order of integration can be interchanged and write

$$\begin{aligned} R_{x\hat{x}} &= \frac{1}{\pi}\int_{-\infty}^{\infty} \frac{E\{x^*(t)\, x(\tau)\}}{t+\sigma-\tau}\, d\tau \\ &= \frac{-1}{\pi}\int_{-\infty}^{\infty} \frac{E\{x^*(t)\, x(t+\sigma+\eta)\}}{\eta}\, d\eta \\ &= \frac{1}{\pi}\int_{-\infty}^{\infty} \frac{R_{xx}\,(\beta)}{\sigma-\beta}\, d\beta, \end{aligned} \tag{1-21}$$

or

$$R_{x\hat{x}}(\sigma) = \hat{R}_{xx}(\sigma) = \hat{R}_x(\sigma). \tag{1-22}$$

Let $x(t)$ be a real valued process, then *property c* can be used to show that x and $\hat{x}$ are uncorrelated. It follows directly from definitions that

$$R_{x\hat{x}}(-\sigma) = -R_{x\hat{x}}(\sigma). \tag{1-23}$$

Therefore, $R_{x\hat{x}}(0) = 0$ and we have established that the time series and its Hilbert transformed time series are *completely uncorrelated.*

(d) The cross-power density spectrum function corresponding to the cross-covariance $R_{x\hat{x}}(\sigma)$ is

$$W_{x\hat{x}}(f) = \begin{cases} -iW_u(f); & f > 0 \\ 0 \quad ; & f = 0 \\ +iW_u(f); & f < 0. \end{cases} \tag{1-24}$$

This statement follows at once from *property c* and *property iii* for Hilbert transforms.

(e) The original time series, $x(t)$, and its Hilbert transform, $\hat{x}(t)$, have identical covariance functions.

From *property c*, we have

$$\hat{R}_x(\sigma) = R_{x\hat{x}}(\sigma). \tag{1-25}$$

Repeating the steps used to demonstrate *property c*, one can show that

$$-R_{x\hat{x}}(-\sigma) = \hat{R}_{\hat{x}}(\sigma), \tag{1-26}$$

or, using Eq. (1-23),

$$-R_{x\hat{x}}(-\sigma) = R_{x\hat{x}}(\sigma) = \hat{R}_x(\sigma). \tag{1-27}$$

Therefore,

$$\hat{R}_{\hat{x}}(\sigma) = \hat{R}_x(\sigma), \tag{1-28}$$

which demonstrates that x and $\hat{x}$ have the same covariance function and hence the same power spectral density function.

(f) Let

$$z(t) = x(t) + i\hat{x}(t), \tag{1-29}$$

then using *properties d* and *e* it follows that

$$R_z(\sigma) = 2[R_x(\sigma) + i\hat{R}_x(\sigma)] \tag{1-30}$$

and

$$W_z(f) = \begin{cases} 4W_x(f); & f > 0 \\ 2W_x(f); & f = 0 \\ 0 \quad ; & f < 0. \end{cases} \tag{1-31}$$

From *Definition 1-2*, the envelope function of a real-valued time series $x(t)$ can be written as

$$\begin{aligned} V(t) &= |z(t)| = |x(t) + i\hat{x}(t)| \\ &= [x^2(t) + \hat{x}^2(t)]^{1/2}. \end{aligned} \tag{1-32}$$

Squaring $V(t)$ and taking expected values produces the result

$$\begin{aligned} E\{V^2(t)\} &= E\{x^2(t)\} + E\{\hat{x}^2(t)\} \\ &= R_x(0) + R_{\hat{x}}(0) \\ &= 2R_x(0), \end{aligned} \tag{1-33}$$

where *property e* has been employed. Hence, one concludes that the ensemble average of the square of the envelope function is equal to twice the ensemble average of the square of the original time series, [5, 6].

(h) Karr has shown an inequality concerning the envelope of a correlation function which follows immediately from our previous results, [7].

The covariance function $R_x(\sigma)$ corresponding to a real valued time random process $x(t)$, can in itself be considered to be a time series in the $\sigma-$ domain. The envelope of the covariance *time* function is obtained by writing

$$|R_z(\sigma)| = |R_x(\sigma) + i\hat{R}_x(\sigma)|, \tag{1-34}$$

or

$$z(\sigma) = [R_x^2(\sigma) + \hat{R}_x^2(\sigma)]^{1/2}. \tag{1-35}$$

The spectral function corresponding to $\hat{R}_x(\sigma)$ is

$$\hat{W}(f) = \int_{-\infty}^{\infty} \hat{R}_x(\sigma) \exp(-2\pi i\sigma f)\, d\sigma. \tag{1-36}$$

From *property iii* for Hilbert transforms

$$\hat{W}(f) = \begin{cases} -iW(f); & f > 0 \\ 0 \quad ; & f = 0 \\ +iW(f); & f < 0. \end{cases} \tag{1-37}$$

Therefore,

$$\begin{aligned} i\hat{R}_x(\sigma) &= i\int_{-\infty}^{\infty} W(f) \exp(2\pi if\sigma)\, d\sigma \\ &= \int_0^{\infty} W(f) \exp(2\pi if\sigma)\, d\sigma - \int_{-\infty}^{0} W(f) \exp(2\pi if\sigma)\, d\sigma. \end{aligned} \tag{1-38}$$

Moreover,

$$R_x(\sigma) = \int_0^{\infty} W(f) \exp(2\pi if\sigma)\, d\sigma + \int_{-\infty}^{0} W(f) \exp(2\pi if\sigma)\, d\sigma. \tag{1-39}$$

Adding Eqs. (1-38) and (1-39) shows that

$$\begin{aligned} R_z(\sigma) &= R_x(\sigma) + i\hat{R}_x(\sigma) \\ &= 2\int_0^{\infty} W(f) \exp(2\pi if\sigma)\, d\sigma. \end{aligned} \tag{1-40}$$

Now,

$$\begin{aligned} z(\sigma) &= |R_z(\sigma)| \\ &= 2\left|\int_0^{\infty} W(f) \exp(2\pi if\sigma)\, d\sigma\right| \le 2\int_0^{\infty} W(f)\, df = 2R_x(0). \end{aligned} \tag{1-41}$$

This is Karr's result which can be written as

$$R_x(0) \ge \tfrac{1}{2} z(0). \tag{1-42}$$

(i) If $x(t)$ is a real-valued random process and is passed through a linear filter with an impulse response $K(t)$, then the pre-envelope of the process after filtering is equal to that obtained by taking the pre-envelope of $x(t)$ as an input.

Let $y(t) = x(t) + i\hat{x}(t)$ be the pre-envelope function of the input waveform $x(t)$. The output after linear filtering is given by the convolution product

$$\begin{aligned} z(t) &= K(t) * y(t) \\ &= K(t) * x(t) + iK(t) * \hat{x}(t). \end{aligned} \tag{1-43}$$

If the input consisted only of $x(t)$, the filtered output would be $x_0 = K(t) * x(t)$. But from *property iv* for the Hilbert transform, $\hat{x}_0 = K(t) * \hat{x}(t)$. Thus

$$z(t) = x_0(t) + i\hat{x}_0(t), \tag{1-44}$$

which proves the assertion.

Instead of characterizing a linear filter by its impulse response function $K(t)$, it is often convenient to deal with the corresponding frequency function $k(f)$. Using *property a,* if $X(f)$ is the Fourier transform of $x(t)$ and $Y(f)$ is the Fourier transform of the pre-envelope function $y(t) = x(t) + i\hat{x}(t)$, then

$$k(f)\,Y(f) = \begin{cases} k(f)\,X(f); & f > 0. \\ k(f)\,X(f); & f = 0. \\ 0 \quad ; & f < 0. \end{cases} \tag{1-45}$$

Therefore, the pre-envelope of the output when $x(t)$ is taken for the input waveform is

$$z(t) = 2\int_0^\infty k(f)X(f)\exp(2\pi ift)\,df. \tag{1-46}$$

Thus the pre-envelope function, $z(t)$, of the output after linear filtering is obtained by taking $x(t)$ alone as an input, doubling the positive terms in the filter frequency response and neglecting negative terms.

(j) If $x(t)$ is a waveform whose frequency spectrum is limited to the range

$$f_0 - \lambda/2 < |f| < f_0 + \lambda/2,$$

then the square of the envelope function corresponding to $x(t)$ is spectral limited so that $|f| \leq \lambda$.

Let $z(t) = x(t) + i\hat{x}(t)$ be the pre-envelope function and focus our attention on the spectral function $G(f)$ of the squared envelope. Thus

$$\begin{aligned} G(f) &= \int_{-\infty}^{\infty} |z(t)|^2 \exp(-2\pi ift)\,dt. \\ &= \int_{-\infty}^{\infty} z(t)\,z^*(t)\exp(-2\pi ift)\,dt. \\ &= Z(f) * Z^*(-f), \end{aligned} \tag{1-47}$$

where $Z(f)$ is the Fourier transform of $z(t)$. Now apply *property a,* and it follows that

$$G(f) = \int_{f_0-\lambda/2}^{f_0+\lambda/2} Z(g)\,Z^*(g-f)\,dg. \tag{1-48}$$

It is seen that $G(f)$ will then vanish for $|f| \leq \lambda$.

1.4 EXAMPLE OF ENVELOPE CALCULATIONS

The definitions and properties of envelope and pre-envelope functions can be applied to derive a well-known result in noise theory. If $x(t)$, a signal consisting of a sinusoid added to a Gaussian process having zero mean value and power density spectrum $W(f)$, is passed through a filter with frequency response $K(f)$, then the first probability density of the output envelope R is

$$f(R) = \frac{R}{\psi_0} I_0\left[\frac{R|z(t)|}{\psi_0}\right] \exp\left[\frac{1}{-2\psi_0}(R^2 + |z(t)|^2)\right], \tag{1-49}$$

where

$$\psi_0 = \int_{-\infty}^{\infty} |K(f)|^2 W(f)\, df \tag{1-50}$$

and

$$|z(t)| = 2\left|\int_0^{\infty} K(f)\, S(f) \exp(2\pi i f t)\, df\right|. \tag{1-51}$$

$|z(t)|$ is the envelope of the input signal in the absence of noise. Let x_0 be the output when only signal $S(t)$ is present and let n_0 be the output of the filter when only a noise signal $n(t)$ is present. Applying *property i*, the pre-envelope of the output signal plus noise has sample functions $(x_0 + n_0) + i(\hat{x}_0 + \hat{n}_0)$. Moreover, $z = x_0 + i\hat{x}_0$. Therefore, the envelope of the output signal is

$$R = [(x_0 + n_0)^2 + (\hat{x}_0 + \hat{n}_0)^2]^{1/2}. \tag{1-52}$$

Now it has been shown that n_0 and $\hat{n}_0$ are uncorrelated. Since n_0 is a linear transformation of a Gaussian process, it then follows that the joint distribution of n_0 and $\hat{n}_0$ is

$$f(n_0, \hat{n}_0) = \frac{1}{2\pi\psi_0} \exp\left[-\frac{1}{2\psi_0}(n_0^2 + \hat{n}_0^2)\right], \tag{1-53}$$

where, using *property i*,

$$\psi_0 = \int_{-\infty}^{\infty} |K(f)|^2 W(f)\, df. \tag{1-54}$$

Define

$$R\cos\theta = x_0 + n_0 \tag{1-55}$$
$$R\sin\theta = \hat{x}_0 + \hat{n}_0.$$

Squaring terms yields

$$n_0^2 + \hat{n}_0^2 = R^2 + x_0^2 + \hat{x}_0^2 - 2R(x_0\cos\theta + \hat{x}_0\sin\theta). \tag{1-56}$$

Observe that

$$|z(t)|^2 = x_0^2 + \hat{x}_0^2. \tag{1-57}$$

Substitute Eq. (1-56) in Eq. (1-53) as a change in variables to obtain

$$f(R, \theta) = \frac{R}{2\pi\psi_0} \exp\left[-\frac{1}{2\psi_0}(R^2 + |z|^2)\right] \exp\left[\frac{R}{\psi_0}(x_0 \cos\theta + \hat{x}_0 \sin\theta)\right]. \tag{1-58}$$

Let

$$x_0 = a \cos \phi \qquad \hat{x}_0 = a \sin \phi, \tag{1-59}$$

where $a = |z|$. Since $a \cos(\theta - \phi) = x_0 \cos\theta + \hat{x}_0 \sin\theta$, the second term in Eq. (1-58) can be integrated with respect to θ to produce

$$\int_0^{2\pi} \exp(b \cos\theta)\, d\theta, = 2\pi I_0(b), \tag{1-60}$$

where $I_0(b)$ is the modified Bessel function of argument b and order zero. When this has been done, the desired result of Eq. (1-49) is obtained.

These same techniques can be easily extended to find the joint frequency function of successive envelope values of noise, or signal plus noise, after passing through linear filters, [8]. Instead of exhibiting these results, it is more illuminating to see just what permits us to obtain closed form expressions for these joint frequency functions.

Let us confine our attention to finding the joint frequency function of successive envelope values of a Gaussian process. The inclusion of a linear filter is of no essential consequence because its only action is a trivial, easily calculated modification of the covariance functions. The first important point is that if we are interested in the joint frequency function for n successive envelope values, R_n, we start by defining $2n$ input signals. This is done in the following fashion:

$$\begin{array}{ll} x_1 = R_1 \cos\theta_1 & y_1 = R_1 \sin\theta_1 \\ , & , \\ \cdot & \cdot \\ \cdot & \cdot \\ \cdot & \cdot \\ , & , \\ x_n = R_n \cos\theta_n & y_n = R_n \sin\theta_n, \end{array} \tag{1-61}$$

where

$$\begin{array}{ll} x_1 = x_1(t) & y_1 = y_1(t) \\ x_2 = x_1(t + \tau_1) & y_2 = y_1(t + \tau_1) \\ , & , \\ \cdot & \cdot \\ \cdot & \cdot \\ \cdot & \cdot \\ , & , \\ x_n = x_1(t + \tau_{n-1}) & y_n = y_1(t + \tau_{n-1}). \end{array} \tag{1-62}$$

Note that $E\{x_n y_n\} = 0$. Since we are dealing with a Gaussian process, if we identify $u_1 = x_1$, $u_2 = y_1$, $u_3 = x_2$, etc., it follows that the $u_1, \ldots, u_{2n}$ form a set of Gaussian distributed variables having the joint frequency function

$$(1\text{-}63) \qquad f_{2n}(u_1, u_2, \ldots, u_{2n}) = \left(\frac{1}{2\pi}\right)^n \frac{1}{|M|^{1/2}} \exp\left(-\tfrac{1}{2}\, \tilde{U} M^{-1} U\right),$$

where the exponent is a quadratic form in $U \cdot \tilde{U}$, the transpose of U is the row matrix $\tilde{U} = (u_1, u_2, \ldots, u_{2n})$ and M is the covariance matrix.

Notice that when the definitions of Eq. (1-61) are substituted in Eq. (1-63), we encounter a set of terms of the form $R_n^2 = x_n^2 + y_n^2$. These terms correspond to the first exponential term in Eq. (1-57). The other terms correspond to the second exponential in Eq. (1-58) and when treated in an analogous fashion give rise to modified Bessel functions.

The reason that a closed form solution can be obtained for the envelope of a Gaussian process is that the frequency functions contain squares of the envelope values R_n. It isn't necessary to compute the square root of the sum of squares, since this procedure does not readily lend itself to an analogous simple computation.

One of the most frequently used results for the joint frequency functions of envelopes of a Gaussian process is that for two envelopes values R_1 and R_2 separated by a time interval τ. The result can be shown to be

$$(1\text{-}64) \qquad f_2(R_1, R_2; \tau) = \frac{R_1 R_2}{\psi_0^2(1 - \rho^2)}\, I_0\left[\frac{\rho R_1 R_2}{\psi_0(1 - \rho^2)}\right] \exp\left[-\frac{(R_1^2 + R_2^2)}{2\psi_0(1 - \rho^2)}\right],$$

where ρ is the envelope of the input signal's correlation function and ψ_0 is the total signal power.

2 CHARACTERISTIC FUNCTION METHOD

2.1 GENERAL REMARKS

There are many nonlinear devices used in physical systems for which no known techniques exist for finding the complete statistical properties of a random process after being transformed by these devices. Fortunately, for a fair sized subset of these nonlinear devices, it is possible to compute expressions for the correlation function of the random process after the nonlinear transformation. Although this provides only limited statistical information concerning the output process, the knowledge of the covariance function is often of practical use in the design and analysis of complex nonlinear systems.

The characteristic function method is one technique for computing the covariance function after transformation of a certain class of nonlinear devices. The technique has proven to be a very valuable tool in the study of nonlinear transformations of random processes, [9, 10, 11, 12, 13, 14]. However the method is not, by any means, a universal technique and the success of the method in a particular application is often dependent on the input process being Gaussian and the Laplace transform of the nonlinear function being such that a certain double integral exists and can be evaluated.

2.2 CHARACTERISTIC FUNCTION METHOD

For notational convenience we will let $y(t)$ represent the input random process to a nonlinear device and $x(t)$ will represent the corresponding process after the nonlinear transformation. This chapter is restricted to the class of nonlinear devices for which the output signal can be written in the form of the Laplace transform:

(2-1) $$x(y) = \mathfrak{L}^{-1}[F(s)] = \frac{1}{2\pi i}\int_{c'} F(s)e^{sy}\,ds,$$

where $F(s)$ is the direct Laplace transform

(2-2) $$F(s) = \mathfrak{L}[x(y)] = \int_0^\infty x(y)e^{-sy}\,dy$$

and c' is a Bromwich integration path parallel to the imaginary axis and to the right of all singularities. While at first thought it may seem that we have restricted ourselves to a very limited class of nonlinear devices, it has been found that many physical situations include nonlinear devices of this type. In fact, the method of the characteristic function, which depends upon having Eq. (2-1) satisfied, has proven to be one of the most frequently used techniques in noise theory.

Make the substitution $s = iu$ in Eq. (2-1) to obtain the form usually taken as the starting point,

(2-3) $$x(y) = \frac{1}{2\pi}\int_c F(iu)e^{iuy}\,du.$$

c is a contour extending from $-\infty$ to $+\infty$ and is idented downward about possible singularities.

Table 2-1 lists $F(iu)$ and the integration path c for several common nonlinear devices, [9].

Suppose we consider an input signal to be a stationary ergodic random process. These restrictions can be relaxed, but it is not necessary to do so for most situations. The correlation function of the output signal can be written as

(2-4) $$\psi(\tau) = E\{x(t)\,x(t+\tau)\}.$$

Substitute the value of $x(t)$ given by Eq. (2-3) and rearrange the terms to obtain the result

(2-5) $$\psi(\tau) = \frac{1}{4\pi^2}\int_c F(iu)\int_c F(iu)\,E\{\exp\,[iuy(t) + ivy(t+\tau)]\}\,dv\,du.$$

The expected value is recognized as the characteristic functon for the sum of the two input random processes $y(t)$ and $y(t + \tau)$. We shall denote this joint characteristic function by $g(u, v; \tau)$. Then Eq. (2-5) becomes

(2-6) $$\psi(\tau) = \frac{1}{4\pi^2}\int_c F(iu)\int_c F(iv)\,g(u, v; \tau)\,dv\,du.$$

This is the fundamental equation for the method of the characteristic function. While the concept and development appears to be almost trivial,

TABLE 2-1

Nonlinear Devices Characterized by Contour Integrals

x	$F(iu)$	C	Nonlinear Device
$x = ay^n$, n is an integer	$\frac{an!}{(iu)^{n+1}}$	Positive Loop about $u = 0$	n'th Power Law Transformation
$x = a(y - B)^2$, n is an integer	$\frac{an!}{(iu)^{n+1}} e^{-iuB}$	Positive Loop about $u = 0$	n'th Power Law Transformation with Bias
$x = 0 \quad y < 0$; $x = ay, y > 0$	$\frac{a}{(iu)^2} = -\frac{a}{u^2}$	Real U Axis from $-\infty$ to $+\infty$, Downward Indentation at $u = 0$	Half-Wave Linear Rectifier
$x = 0 \quad , y < B$; $x = a(v - B)^\nu, y > B$; ν any positive number	$\frac{a\Gamma(\nu + 1)}{(iu)^{\nu+1}} e^{-iuB}$	"	ν'th Power Rectifier with Limiting
$x = 0 \ , y < 0$; $x = ay \ , 0 < y < D$; $x = aD, y > 0$	$\frac{a(1 - e^{-iuD})}{(iu)^2}$	"	Linear Rectifier with Limiting
$x = 0 \quad , y < 0$; $x = \phi(y), y > 0$	$F(p) = \int_0^\infty \phi(t)^{-pt}\, dt$	"	General Half-Wave Rectifier
$x = 1 \ , y < 0$; $x = -1, y > 0$	$\frac{1}{u}; -\frac{1}{u}$	"	Ideal Limiter
$x = \frac{1}{\sqrt{2\pi\beta}} \int_0^y \exp\left(-\frac{z^2}{2\beta}\right) dz$	$\frac{1}{iu} \exp\left(-\frac{\beta u^2}{2}\right)$	"	Smooth Limiter

it has turned out that the fundamental equation leads to one of the most important and useful techniques in the analysis of nonlinear physical systems.

2.3 NONLINEAR DEVICES HAVING GAUSSIAN INPUTS

The one really practical difficulty in applying the characteristic function method is to find a suitable expression for $g(u, v; \tau)$ which is the joint characteristic function of the input random process. As one might expect, the method has met its greatest successes when the input is a Gaussian process. Recognizing this fact, Price has applied the method of the characteristic function to prove a theorem on the output correlation function of nonlinear devices having Gaussian input signals, [15]. This theorem has several interesting applications. Among other properties, it provides an alternate method of finding the correlation function for the output of nonlinear devices without a direct application of the fundamental relation, Eq. (2-6). Furthermore, this theorem also provides additional insight into the type of nonlinear transformations that can be treated by the method of the characteristic function.

The theorem as stated and proved by Price was displayed in all the generality of $n-$ dimensional relations. Since only the two-dimensional results are required for most noise theory applications, we will confine ourselves to the simpler form of Price's theorem.

Suppose $x_1(t)$ and $x_2(t)$ are random variables (zero mean value) taken from a Gaussian process having the joint frequency function

$$(2\text{-}7) \qquad f(x_1, x_2) = \frac{1}{2\pi\sqrt{1 - R_{12}^2/R_{11}^2}} \exp\left[-\frac{1}{2\left(1 - \frac{R_{12}^2}{R_{11}^2}\right)}\left(x_1^2 + x_2^2 - 2\frac{R_{12}}{R_{11}}x_1x_2\right)\right],$$

where

$$(2\text{-}8) \qquad R_{12} = E\{x_1x_2\}.$$

Let x_1 and x_2 be passed through *zero-memory* devices and denote the respective outputs by $h_1(x_1)$ and $h_2(x_2)$. Then the output cross-covariance function can be written as

$$(2\text{-}9) \qquad \psi = E\{h_1(x_1)\, h_2(x_2)\}.$$

Define the nomalized *input correlation* coefficient to be

$$(2\text{-}10) \qquad \rho_{12} = R_{12}/R_{11}.$$

Theorem (Price): *Under the above hypothesis, if the input process is Gaussian and if $h_j(x)$ satisfy certain integrability conditions, then*

$$(2\text{-}11) \qquad \frac{\partial^k \psi}{\partial \rho_{12}^k} = E\{h_1^{(k)}(x_1)\, h_2^{(k)}(x_2)\},$$

where

$$(2\text{-}12) \qquad h_j^{(k)}(x_j) = \frac{\partial^k}{\partial x^k} h_j^{(x)}\big|_{x=x_j}.$$

Moreover, if Eq. (2-11) is satisfied, the original process must be Gaussian.

Assume that each $h_j(x)$ can be represented by the sum of two Laplace transforms. Thus

$$(2\text{-}13) \qquad h_j(x) = \frac{1}{2\pi i}\int_{c_j^+} H_{j^+}(u)e^{iux}\,du + \frac{1}{2\pi i}\int_{c_j^-} H_{j^-}(u)e^{iux}\,du,$$

where

$$(2\text{-}14) \qquad H_{j^+}(u) = \int_0^\infty h_j(x)e^{-iux}\,dx$$

$$H_{j^-}(u) = \int_{-\infty}^0 h_j(x)e^{-iux}\,dx.$$

c_{j^+} and c_{j^-} are the appropriate contours corresponding to the transformations of $h_j(x)$. For the moment, assume that x_1, x_2 have some general joint frequency function, $w(x_1, x_2)$, which need not be Gaussian. Then the output correlation function after the random process has passed through the zero-memory devices can formally be written as

$$\psi = \int_{-\infty}^{\infty} \int_{-\infty}^{\infty} h_1(x_1)\, h_2(x_2)\, w(x_1, x_2)\, dx_1\, dx_2. \tag{2-15}$$

Substitute Eq. (2-13) in (2-15) and use the symbol Σ' to denote summation over all possible $\pm$ combinations resulting from Eq. (2-13). In abbreviated form, we can write

$$\psi = \frac{1}{(2\pi i)^2} \Sigma' \int_{-\infty}^{\infty} \int_{-\infty}^{\infty} \int_{c_1^{\pm}} \int_{c_2^{\pm}} H_{1^{\pm}}(u_1)\, H_{2^{\pm}}(u_2) \exp\,[i(u_1x_1 + u_2x_2)]\, w(x_1, x_2)\, du_1\, du_2\, dx_1\, dx_2. \tag{2-16}$$

Noting that the joint characteristic function of the random variables (x_1, x_2) is

$$g(u_1, u_2) = \int_{-\infty}^{\infty} \int_{-\infty}^{\infty} w(x_1, x_2) \exp\,\{i(u_1x_1 + u_1x_2)\}\, dx_1\, dx_2, \tag{2-17}$$

Eq. (2-16) can be written as

$$\psi = \frac{1}{(2\pi i)^2} \Sigma' \int_{c_1^{\pm}} \int_{c_2^{\pm}} H_{1^{\pm}}(u_1)\, H_{2^{\pm}}(u_2)\, g(u_1, u_2)\, du_1\, du_2. \tag{2-18}$$

The necessary condition for which the theorem is valid will first be established. If the theorem is true, it must hold for the particular value $k = 1$. Using Eq. (2-11) for the case in which $k = 1$, the result is

$$\frac{\partial \psi}{\partial \rho_{12}} = \frac{1}{(2\pi i)^2} \Sigma' \int_{c_1^{\pm}} \int_{c_2^{\pm}} H_{1^{\pm}}(u_1)\, H_{2^{\pm}}(u_2) \frac{\partial}{\partial \rho_{12}} g(u_1, u_2)\, du_1\, du_2. \tag{2-19}$$

The right-hand side of Eq. (2-11), for $k = 1$, is evaluated by using Eq. (2-14). One obtains

$$E\{h_1^{(1)}(x_1)\, h_2^{(1)}(x_2)\} = E\left\{\frac{\partial}{\partial x_1} h(x_1) \frac{\partial}{\partial x_2} h(x_2)\right\}. \tag{2-20}$$

However,

$$\frac{\partial}{\partial x_j} h(x_j) = \frac{iu_j}{2\pi i} \int_{c_j^+} H_{j+}(u_j)\, e^{iu_jx_j}\, du_j + \frac{iu_j}{2\pi i} \int_{c_j^-} H_j(u_j)\, e^{iu_jx_j}\, du_j. \tag{2-21}$$

Insert Eq. (2-21) in (2-19);

$$E\{h_1^{(1)}(x_1)\, h_2^{(1)}(x_2)\} = E\left\{\frac{-1}{(2\pi i)^2} \Sigma' \int_{c_1^{\pm}} \int_{c_2^{\pm}} H_{1^{\pm}}(u_1)\, H_{2^{\pm}}(u_2)\, u_1u_2 \exp\,[i(u_1x_1 + u_2x_2)]\, du_1\, du_2\right\}. \tag{2-22}$$

But since,

$$g(u_1, u_2) = E\{\exp\,[i(u_1x_1 + u_2x_2)]\}, \tag{2-23}$$

interchanging the order of integration in Eq. (2-22) yields

(2-24) $E\{h_1^{(1)}(x_1)\, h_2^{(1)}(x_2)\} =$

$$-\frac{1}{(2\pi i)^2}\Sigma' \int_{c_1^*}\int_{c_2^*} H_{1^*}(u_1)\, H_{2^*}(u_2)\, u_1u_2\, g(u_1, u_2)\, du_1\, du_2.$$

Combine Eqs. (2-11), (2-19) and (2-24);

(2-25) $$\Sigma' \int_{c_1^*}\int_{c_2^*} H_{1^*}(u_1)\, H_{2^*}(u_2) \left[-\frac{\partial}{\partial\rho_{12}} g(u_1, u_2) + u_1u_2 g(u_1, u_2)\right] du_1\, du_2 = 0.$$

Equation (2-25) must have a vanishing quantity within the brackets if it is to hold for arbitrary $h_j(x)$ and hence, arbitrary $H_{j^*}(u)$. This implies that

(2-26) $$\frac{\partial}{\partial\rho_{12}} g(u_1, u_2) = u_1u_2 g(u_1, u_2).$$

Since $\rho_{12} = \rho_{21}$, the solution to Eq. (2-26) is

(2-27) $$\ln g(u_1, u_2) = -\tfrac{1}{2}\rho_{12}\, u_1u_2 + \phi\,(u_1, u_2),$$

where $\phi\,(u_1, u_2)$ is the constant of integration. The constant can be evaluated by considering two limiting cases.

If the x_j are completely correlated, consider the case for which $\rho_{12} = \rho_{21} = +1$. In this situation, the joint frequency function can be written as

(2-28) $$w(x_1, x_2) = w(x_1)\, \delta(x_2 - x_1 + \bar{x}_1 - \bar{x}_2),$$

where $\bar{x}_j = E\{x_j\}$ and δ is the Dirac-delta function. Substitute Eq. (2-28) in Eq. (2-23) to find the joint characteristic function for the special case of complete correlation. Therefore, for $\rho_{12} = +1$,

(2-29) $$g_+(u_1, u_2) = \int_{-\infty}^{\infty}\int_{-\infty}^{\infty} \exp\,[i(u_1x_1 + u_2x_2)]\, w(x_1, x_2)\, dx_1\, x_2,$$

$$= \int_{-\infty}^{\infty}\int_{-\infty}^{\infty} \exp\,[i(u_1x_1 + u_2x_2)]\, w(x_1)\, \delta(x_2 - x_1 + \bar{x}_1 - \bar{x}_2)\, dx_1\, dx_2$$

$$= \int_{-\infty}^{\infty} e^{iu_1x_1} \exp\,[iu_2(x_1 - \bar{x}_1 + \bar{x}_2)]\, w(x_1)\, dx_1$$

$$= \exp\,[i(u_1\bar{x}_1 + u_2\bar{x}_2)] \int_{-\infty}^{\infty} w(x_1) \exp\,[i(u_1 + u_2)\,(x_1 - \bar{x}_1)]\, dx_1$$

$$= \theta(u_1 + u_2) \exp\,[i(u_1\bar{x}_1 + u_2\bar{x}_2)];\ \text{for } \rho_{12} = +1$$

where, by obvious identification,

(2-30) $$\theta(u_1 + u_2) = \int_{-\infty}^{\infty} w(x_1) \exp\,[i(u_1 + u_2)\,(x_1 - \bar{x}_1)]\, dx_1.$$

If the variables are completely correlated and if $\rho_{12} = -1$, then one can think of x_2 as being completely correlated with $-x_1$. By analogy with Eq. (2-29), the corresponding joint characteristic function is

(2-31) $$g_-(u_1, u_2) = \int_{-\infty}^{\infty}\int_{-\infty}^{\infty} \exp\,[i(u_1x_1 + u_2x_2)]\, w(-x_1, x_2)\, dx_1\, dx_2$$

$$= \int_{-\infty}^{\infty}\int_{-\infty}^{\infty} \exp\,[i(u_1x_1 + u_2x_2)]\, w(x_1)\, \delta(x_2 + x_1 - \bar{x}_1 - \bar{x}_2)\, dx_1\, dx_2$$

$$= \int_{-\infty}^{\infty} e^{iu_1x_1} \exp\,[iu_2(-x_1 + \bar{x}_1 + \bar{x}_2)]\, w(x_1)\, dx_1$$

$$= \theta(u_1 - u_2) \exp\,[i(u_1\bar{x}_1 + u_2\bar{x}_2)]; \text{ for } \rho_{12} = -1.$$

Substitute $g_+(u_1, u_2)$ into Eq. (2-27). The result is

(2-32) $$\ln \phi_+(u_1, u_2) = \tfrac{1}{2}\, \rho_{12}\, u_1u_2 + \ln g_+(u_1, u_2),$$

$$\phi_+(u_1, u_2) = \frac{u_1u_2}{2} + \ln \theta(u_1 + u_2) + i(u_1\bar{x}_1 + u_2\bar{x}_2).$$

On the other hand, if $g_-(u_1, u_2)$ is inserted in Eq. (2-27), the result is

(2-33) $$\phi_-(u_1, u_2) = -\frac{u_1u_2}{2} + \ln \theta(u_1 - u_2) + i(u_1\bar{x}_1 + u_2\bar{x}_2).$$

But since Eqs. (2-32) and (2-33) must be compatible for any admissible values of ρ_{12}, it follows that

(2-34) $$\frac{u_1u_2}{2} + \ln \theta(u_1 + u_2) = \frac{u_1u_2}{2} \ln \theta(u_1 - u_2) = M,$$

where M is a constant.

Combine Eqs. (2-27), (2-30), and (2-34) to obtain the necessary conditions for Eq. (2-11) to be true when $k = 1$. It is found that

(2-35) $$g(u_1, u_2) = -\tfrac{1}{2}\, \rho_{12}\, u_1u_2 + i(u_1\bar{x}_1 + u_2\bar{x}_2) + M,$$

or

(2-36) $$g(u_1, u_2) = \exp\,[(-\tfrac{1}{2}\, \rho_{12}u_1u_2) \exp\,[i(u_1\bar{x}_1 + u_2\bar{x}_2)]\, e^{M}.$$

If Eq. (2-36) is normalized by setting $M = 0$, the result is recognized as the joint characteristic function for two correlated Gaussian random variables. This establishes the necessity for the random variables to be jointly Gaussian distributed to satisfy the reduced theorem statement Eq. (2-11).

Finally, it is necessary to demonstrate that Eq. (2-36) is sufficient to satisfy Eq. (2-11). Substitute Eq. (2-36), with $M = 0$, in Eq. (2-18);

(2-37) $$\psi = \frac{1}{(2\pi i)^2} \Sigma' \int_{c_1^*}\int_{c_2^*} H_{1^*}(u_1)\, H_{2^*}(u_2)$$

$$\exp\,(-\tfrac{1}{2}\, \rho_{12}u_1u_2) \exp\,[i(u_1\bar{x}_1 + u_2\bar{x}_2)]\, du_1\, du_2.$$

Therefore, noting that $\rho_{12} = \rho_{21}$,

(2-38)
$$\frac{\partial^k \psi}{\partial \rho_{12}{}^k} = \frac{(-1)^k}{(2\pi i)^2} \Sigma' \int_{c_1^*} \int_{c_2^*} H_{1^*}(u_1)\, H_{2^*}(u_2)\, (u_1 u_2)^k \exp\left(-\tfrac{1}{2}\, \rho_{12} u_1 u_2\right) \exp\left[i(u_1 \bar{x}_1 + u_2 \bar{x}_2)\right] du_1\, du_2$$
$$= \frac{(-1)^k}{(2\pi i)^2} \Sigma' \int_{c_1^*} \int_{c_2^*} (u_1 u_2)^k\, H_{1^*}(u_1)\, H_{2^*}(u_2)\, g(u_1, u_2)\, du_1\, du_2.$$

From Eq. (2-13),

(2-39)
$$\frac{\partial^k h_j(x)}{\partial x^k} = \frac{(iu)^k}{2\pi i} \Sigma' \int_{c_j^*} H_{j^*}(u)\, e^{iux}\, du.$$

Write Eq. (2-38) in the form

(2-40)
$$\frac{\partial^k \psi}{\partial \rho_{12}{}^k} = \frac{(-1)^k}{(2\pi i)^2} \Sigma' \int_{-\infty}^{\infty} \int_{-\infty}^{\infty} \int_{c_1^*} \int_{c_2^*} (u_1 u_2)^k\, H_{1^*}(u_1)\, H_{2^*}(u_2) \exp\left[i(u_1 x_1 + u_2 x_2)\right] f(x_1, x_2)\, du_1\, du_2\, dx_1\, dx_2.$$

$f(x_1, x_2)$ is the joint Gaussian frequency function which now replaces the temporary choice of $w(x_1, x_2)$. Combine Eqs. (2-39) and (2-40),

(2-41)
$$\frac{\partial^k \psi}{\partial \rho_{12}{}^k} = \frac{(-1)^k}{(2\pi i)^2} \frac{(2\pi i)^2}{i^{2k}} \int_{-\infty}^{\infty} \int_{-\infty}^{\infty} \frac{\partial^k h_1(x_1)}{\partial x_1{}^k} \frac{\partial^k h_2(x_2)}{\partial x_2{}^k} f(x_1, x_2)\, dx_1\, dx_2$$
$$= E\left\{\frac{\partial^k h_1(x_1)}{\partial x_1{}^k} \frac{\partial^k h_2(x_2)}{\partial x_2{}^k}\right\}.$$

This completes the proof of the reduced version of Price's theorem.

Before demonstrating the usefulness of Price's theorem, a few additional expressions are derived to expedite the solutions of the illustrative examples.

Since x_1 and x_2 are Gaussian distributed random variables, their joint frequency function is

(2-42)
$$f(x_1, x_2) = \frac{1}{2\pi\sqrt{1 - R^2}} \exp\left[-\frac{1}{2(1 - R^2)} (x_1^2 + x_2^2 - 2Rx_1x_2)\right],$$

where we have assumed the typical normalized situation for which

(2-43)
$$E\{x(t)\} = 0$$
$$E\{x^2(t)\} = 1$$
$$E\{x_1 x_2\} = R.$$

If $x_1 = x(t)$ and $x_2 = x(t + \tau)$, then Eq. (2-11) becomes

(2-44)
$$\frac{\partial^k \psi(\tau)}{\partial R(\tau)^k} = E\{h_1^{(k)}\, [x(t)] h_2^{(k)}\, [x(t + \tau)]\}$$

$$= \iint_{-\infty}^{\infty} \frac{h_1^{(k)}\, (x_1) h_2^{(k)}\, (x_2) \exp\left\{-\frac{1}{2(1 - R^2)} [x_1^2 + x_2^2 - 2R(\tau) x_1 x_2]\right\}}{2\pi\sqrt{1 - R^2(\tau)}}\, dx_1\, dx_2.$$

As illustrated in the examples in the next section, Eq. (2-44) assumes particularly simple forms when the $h_j(x)$ are piecewise-polynomial functions and the order of differentiation, k, is sufficiently large. The simplicity arises because the terms $h_i^{(k)}(x)$ will become δ-functions of various orders and the integral in Eq. (2-44) is then easily evaluated.

A large class of applied noise problems require computation of the derivatives of $\psi(\tau)$ (output correlation function) with respect to τ. This derivative can be found from Eq. (2-44) by applying the standard function-of-a-function differentiation formula in the form

$$\frac{d\psi(\tau)}{d\tau} = \frac{\partial\psi(\tau)}{\partial R(\tau)} \cdot \frac{dR(\tau)}{d\tau}. \tag{2-45}$$

This device enables one to employ Eq. (2-44) to treat nonlinear devices, in some cases, independently of the input correlation function. Moreover, we see that the derivatives of $R(\tau)$ with respect to τ do not involve $h_j(x)$.

2.4 EXAMPLES

Several examples are presented to illustrate how both the method of the characteristic function and the particular specialized version of Price can be used to solve some well-known problems in noise theory. The particular set of problems are not in themselves of too much current interest, but serve as nice illustrations because the covariance functions of the output signals have been evaluated by several of the basic analysis techniques now available for nonlinear transformations of random processes.

(i) *Ideal Limiter*

(a) Characteristic Function Method—The ideal limiter is characterized by the input-output relations:

$$\begin{aligned} x &= 1; \quad y > 0 \\ x &= -1; \quad y < 0. \end{aligned} \tag{2-46}$$

The function $F(iu)$ appearing in the fundamental Eq. (2-6) corresponding to the ideal limiter is seen from Table 2-1 to be $\pm\, 1/u$. If y is assumed to be an input Gaussian process, its joint characteristic function corresponding to sample values $y_1 = y(t)$ and $y_2 = y(t + \tau)$ is, [16, p. 287],

$$g(u, v; \tau) = \exp\left[-\tfrac{1}{2}(u^2 + 2Ruv + v^2)\right], \tag{2-47}$$

where

$$R = E\{y_1y_2\}. \tag{2-48}$$

The output correlation function becomes

(2-49) $$\psi(\tau) = \frac{1}{4\pi^2} \int_c \frac{e^{-u^2/2}}{(\pm)u}\, du \int_c \frac{1}{(\pm)v} \exp\left[-\tfrac{1}{2}(2Ruv + v^2)\right] dv.$$

Integrals of this form arise frequently in noise theory analysis. One procedure in evaluating the double integral is to first expand the cross-product term of the exponential into a power series. This produces

(2-50) $$\psi(\tau) = \frac{1}{4\pi^2} \sum_{n=0}^{\infty} \frac{(-1)^n R^n}{n!} \left[\pm \int_{\pm c} u^{n-1} e^{-u^2/2}\, du\right]^2.$$

The integral will vanish unless $n = 0$, or is an odd integer. When $n = 0$, because of the $\pm$ sign in Eq. (2-49), the two contributions of the residue cancel each other. Replace n by $2q + 1$, and the integral can be evaluated to produce

(2-51) $$\psi(\tau) = \frac{4}{4\pi^2} \sum_{q=0}^{\infty} \frac{(R)^{2q+1}}{(2q+1)!}\, 2^{2q+1}\, \pi \left(\frac{1}{2}\right)_q \left(\frac{1}{2}\right)_q,$$

where the factorial function is defined as

(2-52) $$(a)_n = \frac{\Gamma(a+n)}{\Gamma(a)}.$$

From this definition it can be shown that

(2-53) $$(2q+1)! = 2^{2q} q!\, (\tfrac{3}{2})_q.$$

Therefore, Eq. (2-51) becomes

(2-54) $$\psi(\tau) = \frac{2R}{\pi} \sum_{q=0}^{\infty} \frac{(\frac{1}{2})_q (\frac{1}{2})_q}{(\frac{3}{2})_q} R^{2q}$$

$$= \frac{R}{2\pi} F(\tfrac{1}{2}, \tfrac{1}{2}; \tfrac{3}{2}; R^2).$$

Finally, recognizing the hypergeometric function in Eq. (2-54), the result is, [17]

(2-55) $$\psi(\tau) = \frac{2}{\pi} \arcsin R.$$

(b) Price Method—The appropriate nonlinear functions are defined by

(2-56) $$h_1(y) = h_2(y) = \begin{cases} 1; & y \geq 0 \\ -1; & y < 0. \end{cases}$$

Therefore, $h_1^{(1)}(y)$ and $h_2^{(1)}(y)$ are first order $\delta-$ functions of area two at $y = 0$. Substitute the $\delta-$ functions in Eq. (2-44) and integrate to obtain

(2-57) $$\frac{\partial \psi(\tau)}{\partial R(\tau)} = \frac{2}{\pi\sqrt{1 - R^2(\tau)}}.$$

Since $\psi(\tau) = 0$ when $R(\tau) = 0$,

$$\psi(\tau) = \frac{2}{\pi}\int_0^{R(\tau)} \frac{dR(\tau)}{\sqrt{1 - R^2(\tau)}} \tag{2-58}$$
$$= \frac{2}{\pi} \arcsin R(\tau).$$

This result, of course, is in agreement with Eq. (2-55).

(*ii*) *Linear Detector*

(a) Characteristic Function Method—The linear detector is characterized by the transformation

$$x = \alpha y; \qquad y \geq 0. \tag{2-59}$$
$$x = 0 \;; \qquad y < 0.$$

The system function is listed in Table 2-1 as $F(iu) = -\alpha/u^2$ and the appropriate contour for the integrals in Eq. (2-6) is the real axis with a downward identation at the origin.

When y is a Gaussian process, the output correlation function is given by the multiple contour integral:

$$\psi(\tau) = \frac{\alpha^2}{4\pi^2}\int_c\int_c \frac{1}{u^2v^2} \exp\left[-\tfrac{1}{2}(R_0u^2 + R_0v^2 + 2R_\tau uv\right] du\, dv, \tag{2-60}$$

where R_τ denotes $R(\tau)$.

Following the standard procedure, expand the cross-product term of the exponential function into a power series.

$$\psi(\tau) = \frac{\alpha^2}{4\pi^2}\sum_{p=0}^{\infty} \frac{(-1)^p R_\tau{}^p}{p!}\left(\int_c u^{p-2}\, e^{-R_0u^2/2}\, du\right)^2. \tag{2-61}$$

This integral will vanish unless $p = 1$, or is an even integer. When $p = 1$, the half residue value at the origin is πi. Replacing p by $2q$, the remainder of the integration can be performed yielding

$$\psi(\tau) = \frac{\alpha^2 R_\tau}{4} + \frac{\alpha^2 R_0}{2\pi}\, {}_2F_1\left(-\frac{1}{2}, -\frac{1}{2}; \frac{1}{2}; \frac{R_\tau^2}{R_0^2}\right). \tag{2-62}$$

Using standard transformations and relations for the hypergeometric function [17], $\psi(\tau)$ can be expressed as follows in terms of common functions:

$$\psi(\tau) = \frac{\alpha^2 R_0}{2\pi}\left[\left(1 - \frac{R_\tau^2}{R_0^2}\right)^{1/2} + \frac{R_\tau}{R_0} \operatorname{arcos} \frac{R_\tau}{R_0}\right]. \tag{2-63}$$

(b) Price Method—For this device the functional relations are

$$h_1(y) = h_2(y) = \begin{cases} y; & y \geq 0 \\ 0; & y < 0. \end{cases} \tag{2-64}$$

In this case we must go to the second derivatives of $h(y)$ in order to obtain δ-functions. One finds that $h_i^{(2)}(y)$ are first order δ-functions of unit area at

$y = 0$. Substitute in Eq. (2-44) for $k = 2$ and integrate. The process yields

$$\frac{\partial^2 \psi(\tau)}{\partial R_\tau^2} = \frac{1}{2\pi\sqrt{1 - R_\tau^2}}. \tag{2-65}$$

Solve Eq. (2-65) subject to the boundary conditions:

$$\frac{\partial \psi(\tau)}{\partial R_\tau} = \left[\int_0^\infty \frac{h_1^{(1)}(x)}{2\pi} e^{-x^2/2}\, dx\right]^2 = \frac{1}{4}; \qquad R_\tau = 0 \tag{2-66}$$

$$\psi(\tau) = \left[\int_0^\infty \frac{x e^{-x^2/2}}{2\pi}\right]^2 = \frac{1}{2}\pi; \qquad R_\tau = 0.$$

The net result is

$$\begin{aligned} \psi(\tau) &= \int_0^{R_T} \left[\frac{1}{4} + \int_0^y \frac{dt}{2(1 - t^2)^{1/2}}\right] dy + \frac{1}{2}\pi \\ &= \frac{1}{2\pi}\left[\sqrt{1 - R_\tau^2} + R_\tau \cos^{-1} R_\tau\right]. \end{aligned} \tag{2-67}$$

(iii) Error-Function Characteristic

(a) Characteristic Function Method—Baum, [18], has studied the properties of a smooth limiting function with the nonlinear characteristic specified by an error function:

$$x = h(y) = \frac{1}{M}\frac{1}{\sqrt{2\pi\beta}} \int_0^y e^{-z^2/2\beta}\, dz, \tag{2-68}$$

with the input $y(t)$ being a Gaussian process.

Instead of using $h(x)$ directly, consider

$$h^*(x) = h(x) + \frac{1}{2M}. \tag{2-69}$$

The additional constant is chosen so that $h^*(x) \to 0$ as $x \to -\infty$. The nonlinear function transform, therefore, is

$$F(iu) = \frac{1}{iuM} e^{-\beta u^2/2}. \tag{2-70}$$

Substitute Eq. (2-70) into the basic relation, Eq. (2-6), to obtain

$$\psi(\tau) = \frac{1}{4\pi^2 M^2} \int_c \int_c \frac{1}{uv} \exp\left[-\frac{1}{2}(R_0 + \beta)(u^2 + v^2) - R_\tau uv\right] du\, dv. \tag{2-71}$$

Notice that except for constants, Eq. (2-71) is identical with Eq. (2-49) for the ideal limiter. Although Baum made no use of this similarity in his work it is exactly the reason why the seemingly difficult error function transformation can be treated in such a simple fashion.

Following the steps used in *example i*, we find that Eq. (2-71), when evaluated, becomes

(2-72)
$$\psi(\tau) = \frac{1}{2\pi M^2} \arcsin\left(\frac{R_\tau}{R_0 + \beta}\right).$$

As Baum pointed out, when $\beta = 0$, Eq. (2-72) reduces to the correlation function of the ideal limiter, as expected.

(b) Price Method—The appropriate transformation is, for the given situation,

(2-73)
$$h_1(y) = h_2(y) = \frac{1}{\sqrt{2\pi}} \int_0^y e^{-u^2/2\gamma^2}\, du.$$

Unlike the previous examples, the method of Price does not give quick results because no amount of differentiation will reduce $h_1(y)$ to a constant. The method will still work, although the first integration may not be trivial. We have

(2-74)
$$h_1^{(1)}(y) = \frac{1}{\sqrt{2\pi}} e^{-y^2/2\gamma^2} = h_2^{(1)}(y).$$

Substitute Eq. (2-74) in Eq. (2-44):

(2-75)
$$\frac{\partial\psi(\tau)}{\partial R_\tau} = \frac{1}{2\pi}\sqrt{\frac{a^2 - b^2}{1 - R_\tau^2}} \cdot \left\{ \iint_{-\infty}^{\infty} \frac{\exp\left[-\dfrac{ax_1^2 + ax_2^2 - 2bx_1x_2}{2(a^2 - b^2)} \right] dx_1\, dx_2}{2\pi\sqrt{a^2 - b^2}} \right\},$$

where

(2-76)
$$a = \frac{\{\gamma^{-2}[1 - R_\tau^2] + 1\}[1 - R_\tau^2]}{\{\gamma^{-2}[1 - R_\tau^2] + 1\}^2 - R_\tau^2}$$

$$b = \frac{R_\tau[1 - R_\tau^2]}{\{\gamma^{-2}[1 - R_\tau^2] + 1\}^2 - R_\tau^2}.$$

The trick is to observe that the term in the braces of Eq. (2-75) must equal unity, since it is nothing more than the integral of a second order Gaussian probability frequency function. Thus, from Eq. (2-75),

(2-77)
$$\frac{\partial\psi(\tau)}{\partial R_\tau} = \frac{1}{2\pi}\sqrt{\frac{a^2 - b^2}{1 - R_\tau^2}}$$

$$= \frac{1}{2\pi\sqrt{(1 - \gamma^{-2})^2 - \gamma^{-4}R_\tau^2}}.$$

Integrate and use the condition that $R_\tau = 0$ when $\psi(\tau) = 0$. Then

(2-78)
$$\psi(\tau) = \frac{\gamma^2}{2\pi} \int_0^{R_T} \frac{dR_\tau}{\sqrt{(\gamma^2 + 1)^2 - R_\tau^2}}$$

$$= \frac{\gamma^2}{2\pi} \arcsin\left(\frac{R_\tau}{1 + \beta^2}\right).$$

2.5 COMMENTS

Although the method of the characteristic function is a very general technique for treating nonlinear devices, there obviously are limitations to the method. The first limitation appears to be a practical restriction rather than one of theory. It has turned out that almost all *closed* form solutions result only when the input is taken as a Gaussian process. The difficulty is two-fold. First, joint characteristic functions are hard to come by for a non-Gaussian random process. Second, for non-Gaussian joint characteristic functions, the required contour integrations often do not lend themselves to simple evaluation. Price's method is often a great computational simplification because it already has introduced the properties of a Gaussian process into the basic equations. However, as illustrated in *example iii,* the Price method either fails or is very difficult to carry through if the nonlinear transformation cannot be represented by a polynomial.

3 CORRELATION FUNCTION METHOD

3.1 COMPUTATION OF MOMENTS

In Chapter 2 the discussion was limited to nonlinear devices which could be formulated as Laplace transforms over a suitable integration contour and to input processes for which the joint characteristic function is known. Obviously if one has knowledge of the joint characteristic function he also, at least in principle, knows the joint frequency function through the Fourier transform relation between characteristic and frequency functions. That is, if $g(u, v; \tau)$ is the joint characteristic function for random variates x_1 and x_2, the corresponding joint frequency function is

$$f(x_1, x_2) = \int_{-\infty}^{\infty} \int_{-\infty}^{\infty} g(u, v; \tau) \exp\left[-i(ux_1 + vx_2)\right] du\, dv. \tag{3-1}$$

A practical difficulty, rather than a theoretical concept, is usually the deciding factor in choosing between using the correlation function techniques described in this chapter or using the characteristic function methods of Chapter 2. It is often found that the integrals encountered with one technique cannot be evaluated in *closed form*, while those arising from the other technique can be integrated. These two techniques are essentially complementary.

If $y(t)$ is an input random process, we consider the problem of determining the statistical properties of the output process

$$x(t) = h[y(t)]. \tag{3-2}$$

It is quite simple to write formal expressions for various moments of the output process $x(t)$. These moments are

$$E\{h^n[y(t)]\} = \int_{-\infty}^{\infty} h^n[y(t)] f_1[y(t)]\, dy\, (t), \tag{3-3}$$

where $f_1[y(t)]$ is the probability frequency function of the input random process, $y(t)$.

Similarly, the covariance function after the nonlinear (or linear) transformation is

$$\psi(\tau) = \int_{-\infty}^{\infty} \int_{-\infty}^{\infty} h(y_1)h(y_2)f_2(y_1, y_2; \tau)\, dy_1\, dy_2, \tag{3-4}$$

where

$$y_1 = y(t) \qquad y_2 = y(t + \tau); \tag{3-5}$$

and $f_2(y_1, y_2; \tau)$ is the joint frequency function of y_1 and y_2.

When $h(y)$ is a power of y, such as y^n, $\psi(\tau)$ can usually be calculated in a straightforward fashion from Eq. (3-4). Unfortunately, the practical mathematical difficulties in all but a relatively few cases are such that the evaluation of the resulting integrals cannot be carried through.

3.2 ENVELOPE DETECTOR [9,19,20]

The correlation function of a process that has passed through a linear detector followed by a narrow band filter is of considerable interest because of the common occurrence of this device in many physical systems. Let us assume at this point, without proof, that the correlation function obtained is nothing more than the correlation function of the envelope of the original process.

If the original input signal is assumed to be a Gaussian process, then its joint frequency function for successive values of its envelope is, Eq. (1-63),

$$f_2(R_1, R_2; \tau) = \frac{R_1R_2}{\psi_0^2(1-\rho^2)} I_0\left[\frac{\rho R_1R_2}{\psi_0(1-\rho^2)}\right] \exp\left[-\frac{R_1^2+R_2^2}{2\psi_0(1-\rho^2)}\right]. \tag{3-6}$$

Now apply the fundamental relation Eq. (3-4) for the case in which

$$h_1(y_1) = y_1 \qquad h_2(y_2) = y_2. \tag{3-7}$$

Thus we have, for the present example,

$$\psi_v(\tau) = \frac{1}{\psi_0^2(1-\rho^2)} \int_0^{\infty} \int_0^{\infty} R_1^2R_2^2 I_0\left[\frac{\rho R_1R_2}{\psi_0(1-\rho^2)}\right] \exp\left[-\frac{R_1^2+R_2^2}{2\psi_0(1-\rho^2)}\right] dR_1\, dR_2. \tag{3-8}$$

One integration can be performed by the use of the following integral, [21, p. 393]:

$$\text{(3-9)}\qquad \int_0^\infty t^{\mu-1} I_\nu(\text{at})\text{e}^{-\rho^2t^2}\,dt = \Gamma\left(\frac{\mu+2}{2}\right)\left(\frac{a}{2\rho}\right)^v \exp(a^2/4\rho^2)\,{}_1F_1\left(\frac{\nu-\mu}{2}+1; v+1; -\frac{a^2}{4\rho^2}\right).$$

Using Eq. (3-9) in (3-8) yields

$$\text{(3-10)}\qquad \psi_v(\tau) = \Gamma\left(\frac{3}{2}\right)\psi_0(1-\rho^2)^{1/2} \sqrt{2}\sum_{n=0}^{\infty}\frac{(\frac{1}{2})_n}{(1)_n n!}\left[\frac{-\rho^2}{2\psi_0(1-\rho^2)}\right]^n \int_0^\infty R^{2n+2}\,\text{e}^{-R^2/2\psi_0}\,dR,$$

where

$$(a)_n = \frac{\Gamma(a+n)}{\Gamma(a)}.$$

Evaluating the remaining integral, which is recognized as a form of the Gamma-function,

$$\text{(3-11)}\qquad \psi_v(\tau) = \frac{\pi\psi_0(1-\rho^2)^{1/2}}{2}\,{}_2F_1\left(-\frac{1}{2}, \frac{3}{2}; 1; \frac{-\rho^2}{1-\rho^2}\right).$$

Although Eq. (3-11) is a perfectly good form for the correlation function, it may be instructive to detail how the hypergeometric function can be manipulated to get it into the forms exhibited by other authors.

Apply the following transformation to Eq. (3-11), [17]:

$$\text{(3-12)}\qquad F(a, b; c; z) = (1-z)^{-a}F\left(a, c\text{-}b; c; \frac{z}{z-1}\right).$$

Thus,

$$\text{(3-13)}\qquad \psi_v(\tau) = \frac{\pi\psi_0}{2}F\left(-\frac{1}{2}, -\frac{1}{2}; 1; \rho^2\right).$$

Now use the differential equation, [17]:

$$\text{(3-14)}\qquad (c-a)nz^{c-a-1}(1-z)^{a+b-c-n}F(a-n; b; c; z) = \frac{d^n}{dz^n}\left[z^{c-a+n-1}(1-z)^{a+b-c}F(a, b; c; z)\right].$$

We find

$$\text{(3-15)}\qquad \frac{1}{2\rho(1-\rho^2)^2}F\left(-\frac{1}{2}, -\frac{1}{2}; 1; \rho^2\right) = \frac{d}{d\rho^2}\left[\frac{\rho}{(1-\rho^2)}F\left(-\frac{1}{2}, \frac{1}{2}; 1; \rho^2\right)\right].$$

But, (appendix),

$$\text{(3-16)}\qquad F\left(-\frac{1}{2}, \frac{1}{2}; 1; \rho^2\right) = \frac{2}{\pi}E(\rho),$$

where $E(\rho)$ is the complete elliptic integral of the second kind.

Combining these results,

$$\psi_v(\tau) = \psi_0[2E(\rho) - (1 - \rho^2)k(\rho)], \tag{3-17}$$

where $K(\rho)$ is the complete elliptic integral of the first kind.

The normalized correlation function for the envelope detector is simply

$$\frac{\psi_v(\tau)}{\psi_v(0)} = \frac{\psi_v(\tau)}{2\psi_0} = E(\rho) - \frac{1}{2}(1 - \rho^2)K(\rho). \tag{3-18}$$

Often one encounters a random process in physical situations for which $\rho^2 \approx 1$. For these cases, Eq. (3-18) can be modified to a form which is much simpler for computational use.

The complete elliptic integrals have the following series expansions, [22]:

$$K(\rho) = \Lambda + \frac{\Lambda - 1}{4} k'^2 + \frac{9}{64}\left(\Lambda - \frac{7}{6}\right) k'^4 + \frac{25}{256}\left(\Lambda - \frac{37}{30}\right) k'^6 + \ldots, \tag{3-19}$$

$$E(\rho) = 1 + \tfrac{1}{2}(\Lambda - \tfrac{1}{2})k'^2 + \tfrac{3}{16}(\Lambda - \tfrac{13}{12})k'^4 + \tfrac{15}{128}(\Lambda - \tfrac{6}{5})k'^6 + \ldots,$$

where

$$\Lambda = \ln 4 - \tfrac{1}{2}\ln(1 - \rho^2) \tag{3-20}$$

$$k'^2 = (1 - \rho^2).$$

Retaining only terms of the order of $(1 - \rho^2)$, we find the desired approximation

$$\frac{\psi_v(\tau)}{\psi_v(0)} \approx \frac{3 + \rho^2}{4};\ \rho^2 \approx 1. \tag{3-21}$$

3.3 ENVELOPE SQUARE LAW DETECTOR

In the previous section, the correlation function for a linear envelope detector was obtained. For future reference, we will employ the same procedure for the envelope of a Gaussian process which has been squared. Make the following change of variables in the joint frequency function given in Eq. (3-6) (remember that one must include the Jacobian of the transformation):

$$Q_1 = R_1^2 \tag{3-22}$$

$$Q_2 = R_2^2.$$

The resulting transformed frequency function is

$$f_2(Q_1, Q_2; \tau) = \frac{1}{4\psi_0^2(1 - \rho^2)} I_0\left[\frac{\rho\sqrt{Q_1Q_2}}{\psi_0(1 - \rho^2)}\right] \exp\left[-\frac{Q_1 + Q_2}{2\psi_0(1 - \rho^2)}\right]. \tag{3-23}$$

Applying the basic relation, Eq. (3-4), the desired correlation function is

$$\psi_u(\tau) = \frac{1}{4\psi_0^2(1-\rho^2)} \int_0^\infty \int_0^\infty Q_1 Q_2 I_0\left[\frac{\rho Q_1 Q_2}{\psi_0(1-\rho^2)}\right] \exp\left[-\frac{Q_1+Q_2}{2\psi_0(1-\rho^2)}\right] dQ_1\, dQ_2. \tag{3-24}$$

The integrals can be evaluated by expanding the modified Bessel function into its infinite series representation and then integrating termwise. The result can be written in the form

$$\psi_u(\tau) = 4\psi_0^2(1-\rho^2)^3 \sum_{n=0}^\infty \rho^{2n}(n+1)^2. \tag{3-25}$$

The infinite series can be either recognized or summed in the following fashion. Let $\rho^2 = y$ and consider the expansion:

$$\sum_{n=0}^\infty y^n(n+1)^2 = y \sum_{n=0}^\infty \frac{d^2}{dy^2} y^{n+1} + \sum_{n=0}^\infty \frac{d}{dy} y^{n+1} = \frac{1+y}{(1-y)^3}. \tag{3-26}$$

Hence,

$$\psi_u(\tau) = 4\psi_0^2(1+\rho^2). \tag{3-27}$$

The normalized correlation function is

$$\frac{\psi_u(\tau)}{\psi_u(0)} = \frac{\psi_u(\tau)}{8\psi_0^2} = \frac{1+\rho^2}{2}. \tag{3-28}$$

3.4 LOGARITHMIC TRANSFORMATION

For a Gaussian process, consider the transformation of the envelope variate R, defined by, [23]

$$z = \ln R. \tag{3-29}$$

The desired correlation function is

$$\psi_z(\tau) = E\{z_1 z_2\}, \tag{3-30}$$

where z_1 and z_2 correspond to transformations of the envelope at a time separation of τ units.

Instead of using the direct method of computation of Eq. (3-4), the result will be obtained through an auxiliary function. $\Delta(\tau)$, the *decorrelation function,* is defined and related to the correlation function in the following manner.

$$\Delta(\tau) = E\{(z_1 - z_2)^2\} = 2[E\{z^2\} - \psi_z(\tau)]. \tag{3-31}$$

The problem of evaluating $\psi_z(\tau)$ has in this fashion been transformed to the problem of finding values for $E\{z^2\}$ and $\Delta(\tau)$.

Using the functional relation Eq. (3-29), the moments of z can be calculated from the frequency function of the variate R. Hence,

$$E\{z^n\} = \int_0^\infty [z(R)]^n f_1(R)\, dR, \tag{3-32}$$

where the frequency function of the original envelope R is the well-known Rayleigh Distribution, [9]

$$\begin{aligned} f_1(R) &= \frac{R}{\psi_0} e^{-R^2/2\psi_0}; \qquad R \geq 0 \\ &= 0; \qquad\qquad\qquad R < 0. \end{aligned} \tag{3-33}$$

Substitute Eqs. (3-29) and (3-33) in Eq. (3-32) which then becomes

$$E\{z^n\} = \frac{1}{2^n} \int_0^\infty \left[\ln \frac{u}{2\psi_0}\right]^n e^{-u}\, du. \tag{3-34}$$

The logarithmic factor can be expanded into a polynomial of degree n in $\ln u$. This process yields integrals of the form

$$\int_0^\infty [\ln u]^q e^{-u}\, du; \qquad q = 0, 1, 2, \ldots, n. \tag{3-35}$$

Integrals of this type are readily obtained from the integral representation of a factorial function, [22], by differentiation. Thus

$$\begin{aligned} \Pi(x) &= \int_0^\infty t^x e^{-t}\, dt \\ \Pi'(x) &= \int_0^\infty (\ln t) t^x e^{-t}\, dt \\ &\cdot \\ &\cdot \\ &\cdot \\ \Pi^q(x) &= \int_0^\infty (\ln t)^q t^x e^{-t}\, dt. \end{aligned} \tag{3-36}$$

Placing $x = 0$ in these expressions yields the evaluation of the required integrals.

The first two moments of z are found to be

$$E\{z\} = \tfrac{1}{2}[\phi(0) + \ln 2\psi_0] \tag{3-37}$$

$$\begin{aligned} E\{z^2\} &= \tfrac{1}{4}\{\phi'(0) + [\phi(0) + \ln 2\psi_0]^2\} \\ &= \tfrac{1}{4}\phi'(0) + [E\{z\}]^2, \end{aligned} \tag{3-38}$$

where

$$\phi(x) = \frac{d}{dx} \ln \Pi(x) = \frac{\Pi'(x)}{\Pi(x)}, \tag{3-39}$$

$$\phi(0) = -C = 0.5772 \qquad \text{(Euler's Constant)},$$

and

$$\phi'(x) = \frac{d\phi}{dx}$$

$$\phi'(0) = \frac{\pi^2}{6} = 1.645.$$

As a sidelight, it is of interest to examine the variance, σ_z^2, of the variate z;

$$\sigma_z^2 = E\{z^2\} - [E\{z\}]^2 \tag{3-40}$$

$$= \tfrac{1}{4}\phi'(0) = \frac{\pi^2}{24} = 0.4112.$$

One notices that the variance of the output variable z is independent of the parameter ψ_0 in the distribution of the original envelope variable R.

Now consider the evaluation of Eq. (3-31). The required quantity is represented by

$$\Delta(\tau) = \int_0^\infty \int_0^\infty [z_1(R_1) - z_2(R_2)]^2 f_2(R_1, R_2; \tau)\, dR_1\, dR_2. \tag{3-41}$$

Introduce the following change of variables,

$$u = \frac{R_1^2}{2\psi_0(1-\rho^2)}; \qquad v = \frac{R_2^2}{2\psi_0(1-\rho^2)}. \tag{3-42}$$

Substitute Eqs. (3-29) and (3-42) in Eq. (3-41), which then becomes

(3-43)

$$\Delta(\tau) = \frac{1-\rho^2}{4} \int_0^\infty \int_0^\infty uv \left(\ln \frac{u}{v}\right)^2 I_0(2\rho\sqrt{uv}) \exp[-(u+v)]\, du\, dv.$$

The modified Bessel function is replaced by its series representation and the resulting expression after termwise integration reduces to

$$\Delta(\tau) = \frac{1-\rho^2}{2} \sum_{n=0}^{\infty} \rho^{2n}\phi'(n), \tag{3-44}$$

where

$$\phi'(n) = \sum_{r=0}^{\infty} \frac{1}{(n+r)^2}. \tag{3-45}$$

After further manipulation one can show that

$$\Delta(\tau) = \frac{1}{2}\left[\frac{\pi^2}{6} - \sum_{q=1}^{\infty} \left(\frac{\rho^q}{q}\right)^2\right], \tag{3-46}$$

or, finally,

$$\Delta(\tau) = \frac{1}{2}\left[\ln(\rho^2)\ln(1-\rho^2) + \sum_{n=1}^{\infty} \frac{(1-\rho^2)^n}{n^2}\right]. \tag{3-47}$$

3.5 RANDOM TELEGRAPH SIGNALS

The computation of the correlation function for random telegraph signals is an example of a method that works even when the basic relation of Eq.

(3-4) is not directly applicable, [24, 25]. Random telegraph signals may be conceptually generated in the following fashion. Suppose that a sequence of very narrow spike-like pulses occur with random spacings that belong to a Poisson distribution. The first spike will cause the output wave form of a switching device to take on the value of $+A$. The next spike causes this output to instantaneously change to $-A$. The problem posed is to find the covariance of the output which varies randomly in time between the limits $\pm A$.

Under the conditions stated, the number of changes in sign, n, in an interval $(0, T)$ is Poisson distributed. Therefore, if $P(n)$ is the probability of n crossings, or changes of sign, in $(0, T)$,

$$P(n) = \frac{\lambda^n e^{-\lambda}}{n!}, \tag{3-48}$$

where $\lambda = k|t_2 - t_1|$ is the expected number of events (changes of sign) in the interval (t_1, t_2). $k > 0$ is a constant.

Let

$$P_+ = \text{probability of the output being } x(t_1) = x(t_2)$$

$$P_- = \text{probability of finding } x(t_1) = -x(t_2).$$

P_+ is the result of an even number of sign changes in the interval (t_2, t_1), while P_- is produced by an odd number of crossings. Hence,

$$P_+ = e^{-\lambda}\left(1 + \frac{\lambda^2}{2!} + \frac{\lambda^4}{4!} + \cdots\right) = e^{-\lambda} \sum_{q=0}^{\infty} \frac{\lambda^{2q}}{(2q)!} = e^{-\lambda} \cosh \lambda, \tag{3-49}$$

and

$$P_- = e^{-\lambda}\left(\lambda + \frac{\lambda^3}{3!} + \frac{\lambda^5}{5!} + \cdots\right) = e^{-\lambda} \sum_{q=0}^{\infty} \frac{\lambda^{2q+1}}{(2q+1)!} = e^{-\lambda} \sinh \lambda.$$

The technique will be to find the covariance function by employing the moment generating property of the joint characteristic function, [16],

$$g(z_1, z_2) = E\{\exp i[z_1 x(t_1) + z_2 x(t_2)]\}. \tag{3-50}$$

The possible state combinations are as follows:

	State	$g(z_1, z_2)$	Probability
(a)	$x(t_1) = A$ $x(t_2) = A$	$\exp[iA(z_1 + z_2)]$	$\frac{1}{2}P_+$
(b)	$x(t_1) = A$ $x(t_2) = -A$	$\exp[iA(z_1 - z_2)]$	$\frac{1}{2}P_-$
(c)	$x(t_1) = -A$ $x(t_2) = -A$	$\exp[-iA(z_1 + z_2)]$	$\frac{1}{2}P_+$
(d)	$x(t_1) = -A$ $x(t_2) = A$	$\exp[-iA(z_1 - z_2)]$	$\frac{1}{2}P_-$

Whence,

$$g(z_1, z_2) = \frac{P_+}{2} \{\exp [iA(z_1 + z_2)] + \exp [-iA(z_1 + z_2)\}$$
$$+ \frac{P_-}{2} \{\exp [iA(z_1 - z_2)] + \exp [-iA(z_1 - z_2)]\}$$
$$= e^{-\lambda}[\cosh \lambda \cos A(z_1 + z_2) + \sinh \lambda \cos A(z_1 - z_2)]$$
$$= [1 - \frac{A^2}{2} (z_1^2 + z_2^2 + 2z_1z_2e^{-2\lambda}) + \ldots]. \tag{3-51}$$

The desired covariance function, ψ, is the negative coefficient of the product z_1z_2 because of the moment generating property of the characteristic function $g(z_1, z_2)$. Therefore,

$$\psi(|t_2 - t_1|) = A^2e^{-2\lambda} = A^2 \exp (-2k|t_2 - t_1|). \tag{3-52}$$

Taking the Fourier transform of this last result produces the spectral density function

$$W(f) = \frac{2A^2k}{(\pi f)^2 + k^2}. \tag{3-53}$$

3.6 QUADRATIC TRANSFORMATIONS OF NON-GAUSSIAN PROCESSES

If the input random process to a nonlinear device is non-Gaussian, in general, very little information can be computed concerning the output signal statistics. In the special case of a quadratic transformation, Magness has shown that the output covariance function can be computed even for non-Gaussian input processes if the fourth-order moment of the input process is known. In a sense, the fourth-order moment replaces the input correlation function which for non-Gaussian input processes may not contain sufficient information to compute the output signal's spectrum.

Consider a general input random process, $x(t)$, for which the following moments exist:

$$E\{x(t)\} = 0, \tag{3-54}$$

$$R(\tau) = E\{x(t)x(t - \tau)\}, \tag{3-55}$$

$$M(\tau_1, \tau_2, \tau_3) = E\{x(t)x(t - \tau_1)x(t + \tau_2)x(t + \tau_3)\}. \tag{3-56}$$

$M(\tau_1, \tau_2, \tau_3)$ is the fourth-order moment of the original process $x(t)$ and is the quantity around which a theory will be constructed.

Two properties of M follow immediately from its definition, Eq. 3-56. That is,

(3-57)

(i) $M(\tau_1, \tau_2, \tau_3) = M(\tau_1, \tau_3, \tau_2) = M(-\tau_2, -\tau_1, \tau_3)$,

(ii) $M(\tau_1, \tau_2, \tau_3) = M(-\tau_1, \tau_1 + \tau_2, \tau_1 + \tau_3)$.

Define an auxiliary function M_1 by the following relation,

$$M(\tau_1, \tau_2, \tau_3) = R(\tau_1)R(\tau_2 - \tau_3) + R(\tau_2)R(\tau_3 + \tau_1) + R(\tau_3)R(\tau_1 + \tau_2) + M_1(\tau_1, \tau_2, \tau_3). \tag{3-58}$$

Note that $M - M_1$ is nothing more than the corresponding fourth-order moment when $x(t)$ is a Gaussian process. This is shown in Chapter 6. Thus, if we restrict our attention to moments of order no higher than four, M_1 can be taken as a measure of the departure of $x(t)$ from a Gaussian process.

If $x(t)$ is a random process such that $x(t)$ and $x(t - \tau)$ become stochastically independent as $|\tau|$ increases, it will follow that

$$\lim_{s\to\infty} M_1(a_1 s + b_1, a_2 s + b_2, a_3 s + b_3) = 0 \tag{3-59}$$

for all (a_i, b_i) such that $a_1^2 + a_2^2 + a_3^2 > 0$. Assume that M_1 goes to zero sufficiently rapid to make it an integrable function. Then its Fourier transform, Q_1, will satisfy the transform relations

$$Q_1(\sigma_1, \sigma_2, \sigma_3) = \iiint_{-\infty}^{\infty} M_1(\tau_1, \tau_2, \tau_3) \exp[-i(\sigma_1\tau_1 + \sigma_2\tau_2 + \sigma_3\tau_3)]\, d\tau_1\, d\tau_2\, d\tau_3, \tag{3-60}$$

and

$$M_1(\tau_1, \tau_2, \tau_3) = \iiint_{-\infty}^{\infty} Q_1(\sigma_1, \sigma_2, \sigma_3) \exp[i(\sigma_1\tau_1 + \sigma_2\tau_2 + \sigma_3\tau_3)]\, d\sigma_1\, d\sigma_2\, d\sigma_3. \tag{3-61}$$

Although it is almost self-evident, the knowledge of M is equivalent to specifying $R(\tau)$. This simply follows because

$$R(\tau) = \frac{1}{R(0)} \lim_{s\to\infty} M(0, s, s - \tau) \tag{3-62}$$

and

$$R^2(0) = \lim_{s\to\infty} M(0, s, s).$$

3.6.1 *TRANSFORM THEOREM*

Let $y_1(t), \ldots, y_4(t)$ represent the output from four filters having the frequency responses $G_1(\omega), \ldots, G_4(\omega)$ and center frequencies $\omega_1, \ldots, \omega_4$, when the common input is the random process $x(t)$. The complex filter functions are defined as

$$G_j(\omega) = 1, \quad |\omega - \omega_j| \leq \Delta/2; \quad j = 1, \ldots, 4 \tag{3-63}$$
$$= 0 \text{ otherwise.}$$

The filter impulse response $g_j(t)$ is the Fourier transform of $G_j(\omega)$, or

(3-64) $$g_j(t) = \frac{1}{2\pi} \int_{-\infty}^{\infty} G_j(\omega) e^{i\omega t}\, d\omega.$$

Using the theory of linear filters, the output process is written as

(3-65) $$y_j(t) = \int_{-\infty}^{\infty} g_j(\sigma) x(t - \sigma)\, d\sigma.$$

Note: Infinite integration limits are chosen for notational convenience; $g_j(t)$ is assumed to be zero for future times to allow for filter conditions of physical realization.

Now focus attention on the fourth-order output moment M_0. By definition

(3-66) $$\begin{aligned} M_0 &= E\{y_1^* y_2 y_3 y_4^*\} \\ &= E\Big\{ \int \overset{\infty}{\underset{-\infty}{\cdots}} \int g_1^*(\sigma_1) g_2(\sigma_2) g_3(\sigma_3) g_4^*(\sigma_4) x(t - \sigma_1) \\ &\qquad x(t - \sigma_2) x(t - \sigma_3) x(t - \sigma_4)\, d\sigma_1\, d\sigma_2\, d\sigma_3\, d\sigma_4 \Big\}, \end{aligned}$$

or

(3-67) $$\begin{aligned} M_0 = \iiiint_{-\infty}^{\infty} & g_1^*(\sigma_1) g_2(\sigma_2) g_3(\sigma_3) g_4^*(\sigma_4) \\ & M(\sigma_1 - \sigma_4, \sigma_4 - \sigma_2, \sigma_4 - \sigma_3)\, d\sigma_1\, d\sigma_2\, d\sigma_3\, d\sigma_4. \end{aligned}$$

Substitute Eq. (3-58) into Eq. (3-67). The result is two integrals, the first of which is simply

(3-68) $$\begin{aligned} I_1 = E\{y_1^*(t) y_2(t)\} E\{y_3(t) y_4^*(t)\} + E\{y_1^*(t) y_3(t)\} E\{y_2(t) y_4^*(t)\} \\ + E\{y_1^*(t) y_4^*(t)\} E\{y_2(t) y_3(t)\}. \end{aligned}$$

The second integral can be transformed into

(3-69) $$\begin{aligned} I_2 &= \frac{1}{(2\pi)^3} \iiint_{-\infty}^{\infty} Q_1(\lambda_1, \lambda_2, \lambda_3) G_1^*(\lambda_1) G_2(\lambda_2) \\ &\qquad G_3(\lambda_3) G_4^*(\lambda_3 + \lambda_2 - \lambda_1)\, d\lambda_1\, d\lambda_2\, d\lambda_3 \\ &= \frac{1}{(2\pi)^3} \iiint_{\omega_i - \Delta/2}^{\omega_i + \Delta/2} Q_1(\lambda_1, \lambda_2, \lambda_3) G_4(\lambda_3 + \lambda_2 - \lambda_1)\, d\lambda_1\, d\lambda_2\, d\lambda_3. \end{aligned}$$

Because the Fourier transform of Q is uniformly continuous, we can use the representation

(3-70) $$I_2 = \frac{1}{(2\pi)^3} Q_1(\omega_1', \omega_2', \omega_3') \iiint_{\omega_i - \Delta/2}^{\omega_i + \Delta/2} G_4(\lambda_3 + \lambda_2 - \lambda_1)\, d\lambda_1\, d\lambda_2\, d\lambda_3,$$

where

$$\omega_i - \Delta/2 \le \omega_i' \le \omega_i + \Delta/2; \qquad i = 1, 2, 3.$$

Therefore,

(i) for sufficiently small Δ, I_2 vanishes unless

(3-71) $$\omega_4 = \omega_3 + \omega_2 - \omega_1,$$

(ii) when Eq. (3-71) is satisfied, the triple integral in Eq. (3-70) may be evaluated as $\frac{2\Delta^3}{3}$, producing

(3-72) $$I_2 = \frac{2}{3}\left(\frac{\Delta}{2\pi}\right)^3 Q_1(\omega_1', \omega_2', \omega_3').$$

We can now write the transform theorem as the following two statements:

(3-73) $$\lim_{\Delta\to 0}\left(\frac{2\pi}{\Delta}\right)^3 E\{y_1^* y_2 y_3 y_4^*\} = 0 \qquad \text{when } \omega_4 \neq \omega_3 + \omega_2 - \omega_1;$$

(3-74) $$\lim_{\Delta\to 0}\left(\frac{2\pi}{\Delta}\right)^3 [E\{y_1^* y_2 y_3 y_4^*\} - E\{y_1^* y_2\}E\{y_3 y_4^*\} - E\{y_1^* y_3\}E\{y_2 y_4^*\} - E\{y_1^* y_4^*\}E\{y_2 y_3\}] = \frac{2}{3} Q_1(\omega_1, \omega_2, \omega_3).$$

3.6.2 ENVELOPE RELATION FUNCTION

Magness has shown that for second moments, the transform theorem has the form

(3-75) $$E\{y_1 y_2^*\} = \int_{-\infty}^{\infty}\int_{-\infty}^{\infty} g_1(\sigma_1)g_2^*(\sigma_2)R(\sigma_1 - \sigma_2)\, d\sigma_1\, d\sigma_2 = \frac{1}{2\pi}\int_{-\infty}^{\infty} W(\omega)G_1(\omega)G_2^*(\omega)\, d\omega,$$

where

(3-76) $$W(\omega) = \int_{-\infty}^{\infty} R(\tau)e^{-i\omega\tau}\, d\tau.$$

Analogous to Eqs. (3-73) and (3-74), we have

(3-77) $$\lim_{\Delta\to 0}\left(\frac{2\pi}{\Delta}\right) E\{y_1 y_2^*\} = 0; \qquad \omega_1 \neq \omega_2$$

(3-78) $$\lim_{\Delta\to 0}\left(\frac{2\pi}{\Delta}\right) E\{|y_1|^2\} = W(\omega_1).$$

Combine Eqs. (3-73), (3-74), (3-77) and (3-78) to show that

(3-79) $$E\{|y_1 y_2|^*\} - E\{|y_1|^2\}E\{|y_2|^2\} = \frac{2}{3} Q_1(\omega_1, \omega_2, \omega_3)\left(\frac{\Delta}{2\pi}\right)^3; \qquad \omega_1 \neq \omega_2,$$

and

(3-80) $$E\{|y_1|^4\} - E^2\{|y_1|^2\} = W^2(\omega_1)\left(\frac{\Delta}{2\pi}\right)^2 + \frac{2}{3}Q_1(\omega_1, \omega_1, \omega_1)\left(\frac{\Delta}{2\pi}\right)^3.$$

Thus, the function $Q_1(\omega_1, \omega_2, \omega_1)$ may be interpreted as a measure of the correlation between the squares of $x_1(t)$ and $x_2(t)$. Define the *envelope relation* function by the relation

(3-81) $$F(\omega_1, \omega_2) = Q_1(\omega_1, \omega_2, \omega_1) = Q_1(\omega_1, \omega_1, \omega_2).$$

Note that

(3-82) $$F(\omega_1, \omega_2) = F(\omega_2, \omega_1) = F(-\omega_1, \omega_2).$$

3.6.3 QUADRATIC DEVICES

Let us see how the theory developed by Magness enables one to compute the correlation function at the output of a quadratic device. A general circuit configuration is shown in Figure 3-1.

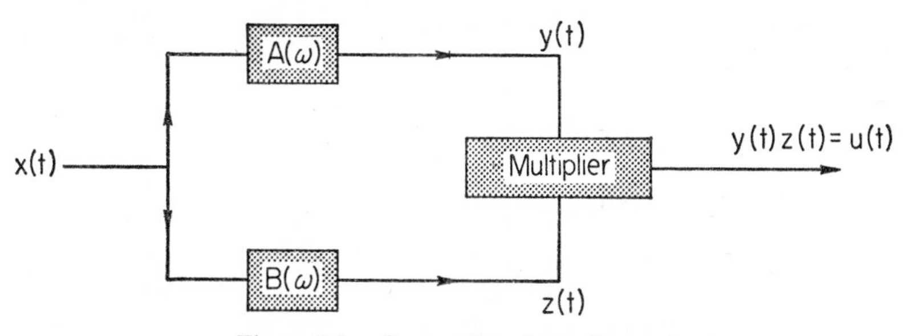

Figure 3-1. General Quadratic System

$A(\omega)$ and $B(\omega)$ are the frequency responses of two general linear filters. Their corresponding impulse responses are denoted by

(3-83) $$a(t) = \frac{1}{2\pi}\int_{-\infty}^{\infty} A(\omega)e^{i\omega t}\,d\omega,$$

$$b(t) = \frac{1}{2\pi}\int_{-\infty}^{\infty} B(\omega)e^{i\omega t}\,d\omega.$$

Thus, the output of each filter can be written as

(3-84) $$y(t) = \int_{-\infty}^{\infty} a(\sigma)x(t-\sigma)\,d\sigma,$$

$$z(t) = \int_{-\infty}^{\infty} b(\sigma)x(t-\sigma)\,d\sigma.$$

These definitions can be combined to obtain an expression for the covariance function for the output signal from the multiplier. We have

(3-85)

$$\psi_u(\tau) = E\{u(t)u(t-\tau)\}$$

$$= \iiiint_{-\infty}^{\infty} a(\sigma_1)b(\sigma_2)a(\sigma_3)b(\sigma_4)$$

$$[E\{x(t-\sigma_1)x(t-\sigma_2)x(t-\tau-\sigma_3)x(t-\tau-\sigma_4)\}$$

$$- E\{x(t-\sigma_1)x(t-\sigma_2)x(t-\sigma_3)x(t-\sigma_4)\}]\, d\sigma_1\, d\sigma_2\, d\sigma_3\, d\sigma_4.$$

Insert Eqs. (3-55) and (3-58) into Eq. (3-85) to obtain

(3-86)

$$\psi_u(\tau) = \iiiint_{-\infty}^{\infty} a(\sigma_1)b(\sigma_2)a(\sigma_3)b(\sigma_4)$$

$$[R(\sigma_1-\sigma_3-\tau)R(\sigma_2-\sigma_4-\tau) + R(\sigma_1-\sigma_4-\tau)R(\sigma_2-\sigma_3-\tau)$$

$$+ M_1(\sigma_1-\sigma_4-\tau,\ \sigma_4-\sigma_2+\tau,\ \sigma_4-\sigma_3)]\, d\sigma_1\, d\sigma_2\, d\sigma_3\, d\sigma_4.$$

The output spectral density function is found from the Fourier transform of $\psi_u(\tau)$;

(3-87)

$$W_u(\omega) = \int_{-\infty}^{\infty} \psi_u(\tau)e^{-i\omega\tau}\, d\tau$$

$$= \frac{1}{2\pi}\int_{-\infty}^{\infty} W_x(\omega_1)W_x(\omega_1+\omega)$$

$$[|A(\omega_1)B(\omega_1+\omega)|^2 + A^*(\omega_1)B(\omega_1)B(\omega_1+\omega)A^*(\omega_1+\omega)]\, d\omega_1$$

$$+ \frac{1}{(2\pi)^2}\iint_{-\infty}^{\infty} Q_1(\omega_1,\ \omega_1+\omega,\ \omega_2)A^*(\omega_1)$$

$$A(\omega_2)B(\omega_1+\omega)B^*(\omega_2+\omega)\, d\omega_1\, d\omega_2.$$

3.6.4 EXAMPLE

The use of the preceding results will be illustrated with an example. Consider a Gaussian process $u(t)$ having moments:

(3-88)

$$E\{u(t)\} = 0$$

$$E\{u(t)u(t-\tau)\} = R(\tau)$$

$$E\{u^2(t)\} = 1.$$

Then

(3-89)

$$x(t) = u^2(t) - 1$$

will be a non-Gaussian process.

Compute

$$(3\text{-}90) \qquad \psi(\tau) = E\{x(t)x(t-\tau)\} = E\{u^2(t)u^2(t-\tau)\} - 2R(\tau) + 1.$$

The expected value can be evaluated using the form for the fourth-order moments for a Gaussian process which was used in Eq. (3-58). The result is

$$(3\text{-}91) \qquad \psi(\tau) = 2R^2(\tau).$$

The fourth order moment of $x(t)$ is much more difficult to obtain. Magness found this moment by resorting to the 8'*th* order moments of the Gaussian process $u(t)$ which were evaluated by differentiating the appropriate characteristic function which served as the moment generating function. He found that

$$(3\text{-}92) \qquad \begin{aligned} M_1(\tau_1, \tau_2, \tau_3) = 16[&R(\tau_1)R(\tau_1+\tau_2)R(\tau_2-\tau_3)R(\tau_3) \\ &+ R(\tau_2)R(\tau_2-\tau_3)R(\tau_3+\tau_1)R(\tau_1) \\ &+ R(\tau_3)R(\tau_3+\tau_1)R(\tau_1+\tau_2)R(\tau_2)]. \end{aligned}$$

The transform of M_1, in this case is

$$(3\text{-}93) \qquad \begin{aligned} Q_1(\omega_1, \omega_2, \omega_3) = \frac{16}{2\pi}\int_{-\infty}^{\infty} [&S(\lambda)S(\lambda+\omega_1)S(\lambda+\omega_2)S(\lambda+\omega_2+\omega_3) \\ &+ S(\lambda)S(\lambda+\omega_2)S(\lambda+\omega_3)S(\lambda+\omega_3+\omega_1) \\ &+ S(\lambda)S(\lambda+\omega_3)S(\lambda+\omega_1)S(\lambda+\omega_1+\omega_2)]\, d\lambda, \end{aligned}$$

where

$$(3\text{-}94) \qquad S(\omega) = \int_{-\infty}^{\infty} R(\tau)e^{-i\omega\tau}\, d\tau.$$

The corresponding envelope relative function is

$$(3\text{-}95) \qquad \begin{aligned} F(\omega_1, \omega_2) = \frac{16}{2\pi}\int_{-\infty}^{\infty} [&2S(\lambda)S^2(\lambda+\omega_1)S(\lambda+\omega_1+\omega_2) \\ &+ S(\lambda)S(\lambda+\omega_1)S(\lambda+\omega_2)S(\lambda+\omega_1+\omega_2)]\, d\lambda \end{aligned}$$

and

$$(3\text{-}96) \qquad \frac{1}{(2\pi)^2}\iint_{-\infty}^{\infty} F(\omega_1, \omega_2)\, d\omega_1\, d\omega_2 = 16\int_{-\infty}^{\infty} [2R^2(\tau) + R^4(\tau)]\, d\tau > 0.$$

4 MULTIPLICATION AND POWER LAW DEVICES

4.1 REMARKS

So many physical systems involve the multiplication of random processes or the raising of signal amplitudes to a power, that a great deal of effort has been devoted to the study of this class of nonlinear transformations. Although many of the general techniques discussed in other Chapters could readily be applied to power law transformations, one can usually more readily apply methods that have been especially developed to treat these transformations. Some of the techniques discussed in this Chapter are applicable to general input random processes. Most, however, work only when the original time series is a Gaussian process.

4.2 A COMMON FALLACY

Most analysts in the field of noise theory are well aware of the theorems governing the addition of statistically independent Gaussian variates. These theorems show that the sum is still a Gaussian variate. Combine these theorems with all the various forms and permutations of the Central Limit theorems, and one is almost led to believe that no matter what you do with Gaussian variates, if you do it enough times the result is almost sure to be another Gaussian variate. As nicely behaved as the Gaussian distribution is, such loose generalizations are just not true. In particular, since it concerns us in this Chapter, the product of two Gaussian distributed variates is simply not again a Gaussian distributed variate.

The joint frequency function of two correlated Gaussian variates with nonzero means is

$$(4\text{-}1)\qquad f(x_1, x_2) = \frac{1}{2\pi\sigma_1\sigma_2\sqrt{1-\rho^2}} \exp\left\{-\frac{1}{2(1-\rho^2)}\left[\frac{(x_1 - x_{01})^2}{\sigma_1^2} + \frac{(x_2 - x_{02})^2}{\sigma_2^2} - \frac{2\rho}{\sigma_1\sigma_2}(x_1 - x_{01})(x_2 - x_{02})\right]\right\}.$$

The frequency function of the product $z = x_1x_2$ is obtained by making a change in variable in Eq. (4-1). It is found that, [26],

$$(4\text{-}2)\qquad f(z, a_1, a_2; \rho) = I_1(z) - I_2(z),$$

where

$$(4\text{-}3)\qquad I_1(z) = \frac{1}{2\pi\sqrt{1-\rho^2}} \int_0^\infty \frac{dx}{x} \exp\left\{-\frac{1}{2(1-\rho^2)}\left[(x - a_1)^2 - 2\rho(x - a_1)\left(\frac{z}{x} - a_2\right) + \left(\frac{z}{x} - a_2\right)^2\right]\right\},$$

and I_2 is the integral of the same function over the range $(-\infty, 0)$. We have used the auxiliary quantities

$$(4\text{-}4)\qquad a_1 = \frac{x_{01}}{\sigma_1} \qquad a_2 = \frac{x_{02}}{\sigma_2}.$$

It is self-evident that the product frequency function $f(z)$ is not a Gaussian function. Craig has shown that for the product $z = xy$,

$$(4\text{-}5)\qquad E\{z\} = a_1a_2 + \rho$$

and

$$(4\text{-}6)\qquad \sigma_z^2 = a_1^2 + a_2^2 + 2\rho a_1a_2 + 1 + \rho^2.$$

As one might expect, it is possible to place restrictions on the original processes so that the product approaches a Gaussian distribution. The following three limiting theorems are due to Aroian, [27].

Theorem 4.1: The distribution of z approaches normality with mean $E\{z\}$ and variance σ_z^2 as a_1 and $a_2 \to \infty$ in any manner whatever, if $-1 + \delta < \rho \leq 1$, $\delta > 0$.

Theorem 4.2: The distribution of z approaches normality with mean $E\{z\}$ and variance σ_z^2 if $a_1 \to \infty$, $a_2 \to \infty$, $-1 \leq \rho < 1 - \delta$, $\delta > 0$.

Theorem 4.3: The distribution of z approaches normality if a_1 remains constant $a_2 \to \infty$, $-1 + \delta < \rho \leq 1$, $\delta > 0$; or if a_1 remains constant $a_2 \to -\infty$, $-1 \leq \rho < 1 - \delta$, $\delta > 0$.

Several of the limiting cases for noise that has passed through a quadratic device could have been very simply evaluated if forms of these theorems had been applied.

4.3 OUTPUT MOMENTS OF A POWER LAW DEVICE

Let us consider the case in which a simple sinusoidal signal is added to a narrow band Gaussian process and passed through a power law device, [28, 29]. The transformation of an input $y(t)$ is represented by

$$x(t) = By^n(t); \quad y(t) \geq 0 \qquad (4\text{-}7)$$
$$= 0 \; ; \quad y < 0,$$

where B is a constant. A choice of odd symmetry of the nonlinear characteristic would merely double the odd harmonic content of the output signal and annihilate the even, while even symmetry would double the even harmonic output and annihilate the odd. The power n can be chosen as any integer subject to the restriction $n > -1$.

The envelope variate for the sum of a sinusoid and Gaussian noise has the frequency function, [19],

$$f(R) = \frac{R}{\psi_0} I_0\left(\frac{RA}{\psi_0}\right) \exp\left[-\frac{1}{2\psi_0}(R^2 + A^2)\right]; \quad R \geq 0 \qquad (4\text{-}8)$$
$$= 0 \; ; \quad R < 0,$$

where A is the amplitude of the sinusoidal signal and ψ_0 is the mean-squared value of the original Gaussian signal which is assumed to have zero mean value. The first order moments of the envelope process are, therefore, given by the expression

$$\overline{R^k} = E\{R^k\} = \int_0^\infty R^k f(R)\, dR. \qquad (4\text{-}9)$$

Substitute Eq. (4-8) in Eq. (4-9), expand the modified Bessel function into its series representation, and finally integrate termwise. The net result is

$$\overline{R^k} = (2\psi_0)^{k/2}\Gamma\left(1 + \frac{k}{2}\right) {}_1F_1\left(-\frac{k}{2}; 1; -\frac{A^2}{2\psi_0}\right). \qquad (4\text{-}10)$$

For the $n'th$ law characteristic of Eq. (4-7), the output moments of the transformed process $x(t)$, are

$$E\{x^n\} = \overline{x^n} = B^n\overline{R^{kn}}. \qquad (4\text{-}11)$$

Thus we find the interesting fact that the $n'th$ moment of the distribution of a process after a $k'th$ law rectifier is simply the $kn'th$ first order moment of the output of a half-wave linear detector (or rectifier). Using this result, we can immediately write

$$\overline{x^n} = B^n(2\psi_0)^{nk/2}\Gamma\left(1 + \frac{nk}{2}\right) {}_1F_1\left(-\frac{nk}{2}; 1; -\frac{A^2}{2\psi_0}\right). \qquad (4\text{-}12)$$

If we now consider the assumption that the input noise bandwidth is small, implying also that ψ_0 is small, then the theorems in Sec. 4.1 indicate that the distribution of $x(t)$ might be expected to tend toward normality. This line of reasoning is based upon the concept that a power law device can be thought of as consisting of a successive process of multiplication. Assuming that the output distribution tends toward the normal distribution for narrow bandwidths, the frequency function of the output process can be represented by an Edgeworth series where the coefficients are the moments determined from Eq. (4-12), [16]. Therefore, we can write the frequency function of the output process in the form

$$f(u) \approx \left[\phi(u) - \frac{\alpha_3}{3!} \phi^3(u) + \frac{(\alpha_4 - 3)}{4!} \phi^4(u) + \frac{10}{6!} \alpha_3^2 \phi^6(u) \right], \tag{4-13}$$

where

$$u = \frac{x - E\{x\}}{\psi_0} \tag{4-14}$$

$$\phi(u) = \frac{1}{2\pi} e^{-u^2/2}$$

$$\phi^n(u) = \frac{d^n}{dy^n} \phi(y) = (-1)^n (2\pi)^{-1/2} e^{-u^2/2} H_n(u),$$

and α_3 is the third standard central moment while α_4 is the fourth standard central moment. $H_n(u)$ is the Hermite polynomial of order n and argument u.

The confluent hypergeometric function appearing in Eq. (4-10) can be readily expanded into tabulated functions for particular values of k, [Appendix, 19]. For example

(4-15)

$$F\left(-\frac{1}{2}, 1; -z\right) = e^{-z/2} \left[(1 + z) I_0\left(\frac{z}{2}\right) + z I_1\left(\frac{z}{2}\right) \right],$$

$$F\left(-\frac{3}{2}, 1; -z\right) = e^{-z/2} \left[\left(\frac{2}{3} z^2 + 2z + 1\right) I_0\left(\frac{z}{2}\right) + \left(\frac{2}{3} z^2 + \frac{4}{3} z\right) I_1\left(\frac{z}{2}\right) \right].$$

4.4 SERIES REPRESENTATION OF A RANDOM PROCESS

Fourier series are an important analytical tool in ordinary functional analysis and one can readily see that a similar type of series representation could be exceedingly useful when working with random processes. In fact, the representation of a random process used in Eq. (1-2) is of this type.

As a mathematical preliminary to other sections, a series representation will be formulated for a complex (or real) wide sense stationary random process on a finite interval using a generalized Fourier-type expansion with independent coefficients. Several investigators have independently established the essential form of the expansion for finite intervals, [30, 31, 32]. Recently the same type of expansion has been extended to vector form, [33].

Let $z(t)$ be a complex, wide sense stationary stochastic process having the properties

$$\begin{aligned} E\{z(t)\} &= 0 \\ E\{|z(t)|^2\} &= R(0) \\ E\{z(t)z^*(t+\tau)\} &= R(\tau) \\ \lim_{t-s\to 0} E\{|z(t)-z(s)|^2\} &= 0; \qquad \text{continuity condition.} \end{aligned} \tag{4-16}$$

We will obtain a series representation for the process $z(t)$ on the interval $0 \leq t \leq T$. For the defined process it can be shown that, [34]

(i) $R(\tau) = R^*(-\tau)$; covariance function is Hermitian symmetric;
(ii) $R(\tau)$ is positive semidefinite; i.e., for every L^2 function $g(t)$ on $(0, T)$

$$\int_0^T \int_0^T g(t)g^*(s)R(s-t)\,ds\,dt \geq 0.$$

The series expansion of $z(t)$ will depend upon the eigenfunctions and eigenvalues of the following homogeneous integral equation with the Hermitian symmetric kernel, $R(\tau)$.

$$\lambda^2 f(s) = \int_0^T R(s-t)f(t)\,dt. \tag{4-17}$$

The development requires use of three properties characteristic of homogeneous integral equations of the type given by Eq. (4-17), [35]. These are:

(a) Eigenfunctions are mutually orthogonal.
(b) Eigenvalues are all real.
(c) Mercer's theorem can be applied to express the positive semidefinite kernel, which is continuous on the space $(0, T) \times (0, T)$, as

$$R(s-t) = \sum_{j=1}^{\infty} \lambda_j^2 f_j^*(s) f_j(t), \tag{4-18}$$

where the series converges absolutely and uniformly on the space $(0, T) \times (0, T)$.

Let $\{G_n\}$ be a set of orthogonal random variables having zero mean value and unit variance. That is,

$$\begin{aligned} E\{G_j\} &= 0 \\ E\{G_j^* G_i\} &= \delta_{ji} \end{aligned} \tag{4-19}$$

where δ_{ji} is the Kronecker-delta symbol.

Consider the series representation

$$z(t) \backsim \lim_{N \to \infty} \sum_{j=1}^{N} \lambda_j G_j f_j(t). \tag{4-20}$$

It is easy to show that this representation produces the required covariance. One simply computes

$$E\{z(t)z^*(s)\} = E\left\{\sum_{j=1}^{\infty} \sum_{i=1}^{\infty} \lambda_j \lambda_i G_i G_j^* f_i(t) f_j^*(s)\right\} \tag{4-21}$$

$$= \sum_{j=1}^{\infty} \lambda_j^2 f_j(t) f_j^*(s) = R(s - t).$$

If the series in Eq. (4-20) is to represent $z(t)$, the Fourier-type coefficients are

$$\lambda_j G_j = \int_0^T z(t) f_j^*(t)\, dt, \tag{4-22}$$

and

$$E\{z(t)G_j^*\} = \lambda_j f_j(t). \tag{4-23}$$

These integrals exist because $f_j(t)$ is continuous on $(0, T)$ and we assumed a continuity condition, Eq. (4-16), for $z(t)$. The series representation converges in the mean to $z(t)$ since,

$$\lim_{N \to \infty} E\left\{\left|z(t) - \sum_{j=1}^{N} \lambda_j G_j f_j(t)\right|^2\right\} = R(0) - \lim_{N \to \infty} \sum_{j=1}^{N} \lambda_j^2 |f_j(t)|^2. \tag{4-24}$$

Mercer's theorem implies that the last limit converges absolutely and uniformly to $R(0)$ showing that the series represents the random process $z(t)$ in the mean limit sense.

If $\{G_n\}$ were chosen as a set of independent Gaussian random variables, then Eq. (4-20) would be a series representation of a Gaussian process.

This series representation is in essence the equivalence of the stochastic integral representation for a wide sense stationary process, [34]. In fact one could almost as easily have started with the integral and obtained the equivalent series form.

4.5 SQUARING AND FILTERING

If there is a *classic problem* in noise theory it certainly would be that in which noise has been processed by a square law device followed by a linear filter. The system is represented in Figure 4-1. This practical system problem was first solved in a rather unique and elegant fashion by Kac and Siegert, [36]. Several modifications of the original method and solution techniques have since been made, [37, 38, 39, 40]. The square law problem has served often as an illustration for other analytical techniques because it is one of the few physically motivated situations for

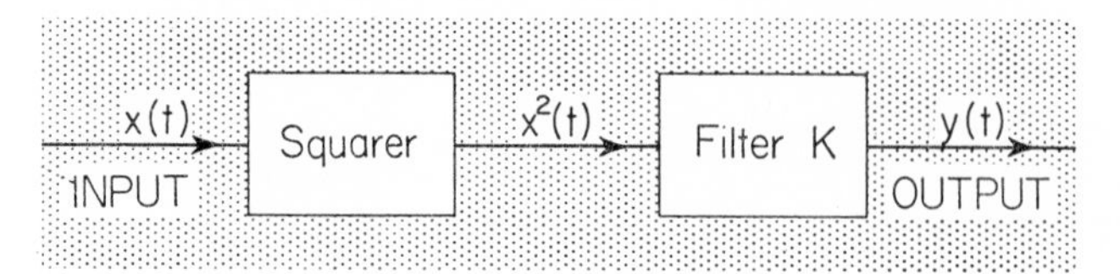

Figure 4-1. Squarer and Filter

which a complete answer is known and it can thus be used for comparison of results.

Suppose that the input process $x(t)$, in Figure 4-1, is Gaussian with zero mean and unit variance. The output process after filtering can be written in the form

$$y(t) = \int_0^t k(t - \tau)x^2(\tau)\,d\tau. \tag{4-25}$$

In this case, as in many other instances after nonlinear transformations, it is difficult, if not impossible, to directly obtain closed forms for the output probability frequency functions. Instead, we go after the characteristic function. Thus we investigate

$$\begin{aligned} g_y(u) &= E\{\exp[iuy(t)]\} \\ &= E\left\{\exp\left[iu \int_0^t k(t - \tau)x^2(\tau)\,d\tau\right]\right\}. \end{aligned} \tag{4-26}$$

The method, introduced by Kac and Siegert, is to use the technique described in Sec. 4.2 to expand $x(\tau)$; $0 \leq \tau \leq t$ into a series expansion in terms of the eigenfunctions of the integral equation

$$\lambda_j\phi_j(\tau) = \int_0^t k(t - \tau)R(\eta - \tau)\phi_j(\eta)\,d\eta, \tag{4-27}$$

where

$$R(\eta - \tau) = E\{x(\eta)x(\tau)\} \tag{4-28}$$

is the covariance function of the input process. We can, therefore, write the series expansion, corresponding to Eq. (4-20),

$$x(\tau) = \sum_{j=1}^{\infty} \lambda_j^{1/2} G_j \phi_j(\tau). \tag{4-29}$$

Since the eigenfunctions $\phi_j(t)$ are orthogonal with weight $k(t - \tau)$, the independent Gaussian variates are found from Eq. (4-29) to be

$$\lambda_j^{1/2} G_j = \int_0^t k(t - \tau)x(\tau)\phi_j(\tau)\,d\tau. \tag{4-30}$$

Insert Eq. (4-29) in (4-25):

$$y(t) = \int_0^t k(t - \tau) \sum_{i,j=1}^{\infty} \lambda_i^{1/2}\lambda_j^{1/2} G_i G_j \phi_i(\tau)\phi_j(\tau)\,d\tau. \tag{4-31}$$

Because of the orthogonality of the ϕ_i, Eq. (4-31) reduces to

$$y(t) = \sum_{j=1}^{\infty} \lambda_j G_j^2. \tag{4-32}$$

Insert this into Eq. (4-27):

$$g_y(u) = E\left\{\exp\left[iu \sum_{j=1}^{\infty} \lambda_j G_j^2\right]\right\}. \tag{4-33}$$

Because of the statistical independence of the set of variates $\{G_n\}$, the characteristic function Eq. (4-33) can be written in the product form:

$$\begin{aligned} g_y(u) &= \prod_{j=1}^{\infty} E\{\exp[iu\lambda_j G_j^2]\} \\ &= \prod_{j=1}^{\infty} (1 - 2iu\lambda_j)^{-1/2}. \end{aligned} \tag{4-34}$$

The original method used by Kac and Siegert at this point completed the problem by solving the homogeneous integral equation, Eq. (4-27), and then evaluated the infinite product form of Eq. (4-34). Siegert [37] showed that an alternate method is possible in which the problem of solving the homogeneous equation and evaluating an infinite product is replaced by one requiring the solution of an inhomogeneous equation followed by an evaluation of a double integral. This alternate approach will be demonstrated.

Observe that

$$\frac{1}{i}\frac{\partial}{\partial u} \ln \prod_{j=1}^{\infty} (1 - 2iu\lambda_j) = \sum_{j=1}^{\infty} \frac{\lambda_j}{1 - 2iu\lambda_j}. \tag{4-35}$$

Using the orthogonality property of the eigenfunctions, we can write

$$\sum_{j=1}^{\infty} \frac{\lambda_j}{1 - 2iu\lambda_j} = \sum_{j=1}^{\infty} \int_0^t \frac{\lambda_j}{1 - 2iu\lambda_j} \phi_j(\tau)\phi_j(\tau)k(t - \tau)\, d\tau. \tag{4-36}$$

It will now be shown that

$$G(\tau_1, \tau_2; u) = \sum_{j=1}^{\infty} \frac{\lambda_j}{1 - 2iu\lambda_j} \phi_j(\tau_1)\phi_j(\tau_2) \tag{4-37}$$

is essentially the Volterra reciprocal function of the kernel $k(t - \tau)R(\eta - \tau)$ in Eq. (4-27), if $\phi_j(\tau)$ and λ_j are its eigenfunctions and eigenvalues. This can be seen by using the original integral equation, Eq. (4-27), to evaluate

$$G(\tau, \tau_2; u) - 2iu \int_0^t k(t - \tau_1)R(\tau_1 - \tau)G(\tau_1, \tau_2; u)\, d\tau_1. \tag{4-38}$$

The result is

$$\begin{aligned} \sum_j \left\{\frac{\lambda_j}{1 - 2iu\lambda_j} [\phi_j(\tau)\phi_j(\tau_2) - 2iu\phi_j(\tau)\phi_j(\tau_2)]\right\} \\ = \sum_j \lambda_j\phi_j(\tau)\phi_j(\tau_2) = R(\tau - \tau_2). \end{aligned} \tag{4-39}$$

Therefore, the function $G(\tau_1, \tau_2; u)$ is the solution to the following integral equation:

(4-40)

$$G(\tau, \tau_2; u) - 2iu \int_0^t k(t - \tau_1)R(\tau_1 - \tau)g(\tau_1, \tau_2; u)\, d\tau_1 = R(\tau - \tau_2).$$

Combining these results the infinite product in Eq. (4-34) can be written as

$$\prod_{j=1}^{\infty} (1 - 2iu\lambda)^{-1/2} = \exp\left[i \int_0^u d\eta \int_0^t k(t - \tau)G(\tau, \tau; \eta)\, d\tau\right], \tag{4-41}$$

since

$$\frac{1}{i}\frac{\partial}{\partial u} \ln \prod_{j=1}^{\infty} (1 - 2iu\lambda_j)^{-1/2} = \int_0^t k(t - \tau)G(\tau, \tau; u)\, d\tau, \tag{4-42}$$

and, therefore,

$$\ln \prod_{j=1}^{\infty} (1 - 2iu\lambda_j)^{-1/2} = i \int_0^u d\eta \int_0^t k(t - \tau)G(\tau, \tau; u)\, d\tau. \tag{4-43}$$

This is the desired result.

4.6 REDUCTION TO DIFFERENTIAL EQUATION

Siegert has gone a step further and has shown that for most practical linear filters, the integral equation, Eq. (4-40), reduces to a differential equation, [37]. This is of practical rather than only theoretical importance because differential equations are often easier to solve than are inhomogeneous integral equations.

The input covariance function $R(\eta, \tau)$ given in Eq. (4-28) can be written as the Fourier transform of the corresponding spectral density function $W(f)$. That is,

$$R(\eta - \tau) = \frac{1}{2\pi} \int_{-\infty}^{\infty} W(f) \exp\left[if(\eta - \tau)\right] df. \tag{4-44}$$

A reasonable restriction, because it suffices for most physical situations, is to limit ourselves to functions $W(f)$ which can be written as the quotient of two polynomials $P_1(f)$ and $P_2(f)$, or

$$W(f) = \frac{P_1(f^2)}{P_2(f^2)}. \tag{4-45}$$

In order to arrive at a meaningful result, $P_2(f)$ must not be of lower degree than $P_1(f)$. Formally define two differential operations

$$P_1\left(-\frac{d^2}{d\tau^2}\right) \quad \text{and} \quad P_2\left(-\frac{d^2}{d\tau^2}\right) \tag{4-46}$$

by replacing f^2 by $-\frac{d^2}{d\tau^2}$ in the two polynomials. The transform relation becomes

$$\text{(4-47)} \qquad \frac{P_2\left(-\frac{d^2}{d\tau^2}\right)}{P_1\left(-\frac{d^2}{d\tau^2}\right)} R(\eta - \tau) = \frac{1}{2\pi}\int_{-\infty}^{\infty} W(f)\,\frac{P_1(f)}{P_2(f)} \exp\,[if(\eta - \tau)]\,df$$

$$= \frac{1}{2\pi}\int_{-\infty}^{\infty} \exp\,[if(\eta - \tau)]\,df$$

$$= \delta(\eta - \tau),$$

where $\delta(\eta - \tau)$ is the Dirac-delta function. Using this operator, the integral equation, Eq. (4-40), reduces to

$$\text{(4-48)} \qquad \left[P_2\left(-\frac{d^2}{d\tau^2}\right) - 2iuP_1\left(-\frac{d^2}{d\tau^2}\right)k(\tau)\right]G(\tau, \tau_2; u) = P_1\left(-\frac{d^2}{d\tau^2}\right)\delta(\eta - \tau).$$

Therefore, the problem of solving the integral equation has been replaced by the problem of finding the two solutions of the linear differential equation

$$\text{(4-49)} \qquad (P_2 - 2iuP_1k)G = 0,$$

valid for $\tau < \tau_2$ and $\tau > \tau_2$ and then properly matching these solutions at $\tau = \tau_2$.

4.7 SOLUTION USING CUMULANTS

Emerson modified the Kac-Siegert solution for the square law device to avoid having to solve an integral equation, [39]. His method depends on the fact that the cumulants of the output distribution are rather simply related to a system operator so that by employing any of the well-known orthonormal systems for expanding frequency functions, i.e., Gram-Charlier, Laguerre, etc., one can compute the output frequency function to any desired degree of accuracy by straightforward techniques. As a simple generalization of the original problem, a filter will precede the squarer as shown in Figure 4-2.

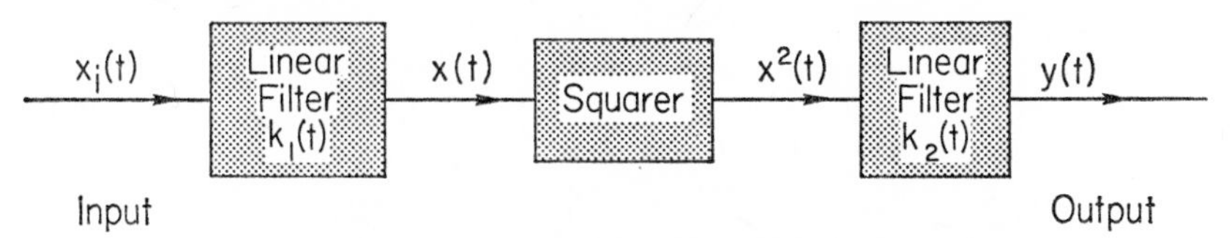

Figure 4-2. Squarer and Two Filters

The output of the first linear filter is

$$x(t) = \int_0^t k_1(t - \tau)x_i(\tau)\,d\tau. \tag{4-50}$$

The output of the squarer is

$$x^2(t) = \int_0^t \int_0^t k_1(t - \tau)k_2(t - \sigma)x_i(\tau)x_i(\sigma)\,d\sigma\,d\tau. \tag{4-51}$$

The output process is

$$y(t) = \int_0^t k_2(t - \tau)x^2(\tau)\,d\tau. \tag{4-52}$$

Substitute Eq. (4-51) in (4-52) and make a change of variable to find

$$y(t) = \int_0^t \int_0^t x_i(t - u)h(u, v)x_i(t - v)\,du\,dv, \tag{4-53}$$

where

$$h(u, v) = \int_0^t k_1(u - z)k_2(z)k_1(v - z)\,dz. \tag{4-54}$$

The right-hand side of Eq. (4-53) is called the system operator, and the function $h(u, v)$, the system kernel.

We now represent the system kernel by the series

$$h(u, v) = \sum_{j=0}^{\infty} \lambda_j a_j(u)a_j(v), \tag{4-55}$$

where the $a_j(u)$ and λ_j are the eigenfunctions and eigenvalues corresponding to the integral equation

$$\lambda a(u) = \int_{-\infty}^{\infty} h(u, v)a(u)\,dv. \tag{4-56}$$

The series expansion exists because $h(u, v)$ is symmetric and positive semidefinite.

Insert Eq. (4-55) in Eq. (4-53):

$$\begin{aligned} y(t) &= \sum_{j=0}^{\infty} \int_0^t \int_0^t x_i(t - u)x_i(t - v)\lambda_j a_j(u)a_j(v)\,du\,dv \\ &= \sum_{j=0}^{\infty} \lambda_j \left[\int_0^t x_i(t - u)a_j(u)\,du\right]^2. \end{aligned} \tag{4-57}$$

Write the input $x_i(t)$ as the sum of a signal plus noise, or in symbols

$$x_i(t) = S(t) + N(t). \tag{4-58}$$

Combine Eq. (4-58) and (4-57) to obtain

$$y(t) = \sum_{j=0}^{\infty} \lambda_j[\sigma_j(t) + \eta_j(t)]^2, \tag{4-59}$$

where

$$\sigma_j(t) = \int_0^t S(t - u)a_j(u)\,du \tag{4-60}$$

and

$$\eta_j(t) = \int_0^t N(t-u)a_j(u)\,du. \tag{4-61}$$

Let the noise be a Gaussian process with the property

$$E\{N(t_1)N(t_2)\} = \psi_0\,\delta(t_1 - t_2), \tag{4-62}$$

where ψ_0 is the noise power per unit frequency and δ is the Dirac-delta operator. Furthermore, because the functions a_j are orthogonal

$$E\{\eta_j(t)\eta_k(t)\} = \psi_0\,\delta_{jk}. \tag{4-63}$$

Thus the row vector $\eta(t) = [\eta_1(t), \eta_2(t), \ldots]$ has as its frequency function

$$f[\eta(t)] = \prod_j \frac{1}{\sqrt{2\pi\psi_0}} \exp\left[-\frac{\eta_j^2(t)}{2\psi_0}\right]. \tag{4-64}$$

The characteristic function of the output process $y(t)$ can now be formulated as

$$g(u,t) = E\{\exp[iuy(t)]\} \tag{4-65}$$

$$= \int \overset{\infty}{\underset{-\infty}{\cdots}} \int \exp\left\{iu \sum_j \lambda_j[\sigma_j(t) + \eta_j(t)]^2\right\} \cdot \prod_j (2\pi\psi_0)^{-1/2} \exp\left[-\frac{\eta_j^2}{2\psi_0}\right] d\eta_j.$$

This integral can be evaluated by completing the squares in the exponential. One finds

$$g(u,t) = \prod_j (1 - 2iu\lambda_j\psi_0)^{-1/2} \exp\left[\frac{\sigma_j^2(t)}{2\psi_0} \cdot \frac{2iu\lambda_j\psi_0}{1 - 2iu\lambda_j\psi_0}\right]. \tag{4-66}$$

The cumulants, k_n, of a distribution are related to the characteristic function through the series expansion of the characteristic function:

$$g(u) = \exp\left[\sum_{n=1}^{\infty} k_n \frac{(iu)^n}{n!}\right]. \tag{4-67}$$

Take the logarithm of $g(u, t)$ in Eq. (4-66) and expand it in powers of (iu) to obtain

$$k_n(t) = (2\psi_0)^n \frac{(n-1)!}{2} \sum_j \lambda_j^n + (2\psi_0)^{n-1} n! \sum_j \lambda_j^n \sigma_j^2(t). \tag{4-68}$$

Define an auxiliary quantity h^n, the $n-$ iterated kernel, by the expression

$$h^n(u,v) = \int \overset{\infty}{\underset{-\infty}{\cdots}} \int h(u,\tau_1)h(\tau_1,\tau_2) \ldots h(\tau_{n-1},v)\,d\tau_1 \ldots d\tau_{n-1}. \tag{4-69}$$

Using Eq. (4-55), it can be verified that

$$\sum_j \lambda_j^n = \int_{-\infty}^{\infty} h^n(u,u)\,du, \tag{4-70}$$

and

$$\sum_j \lambda_j^n \sigma_j^2(t) = \iint_{-\infty}^{\infty} S(t-u)h^n(u,v)S(t-v)\,du\,dv. \tag{4-71}$$

Inserting these expressions in Eq. (4-68), the *n'th* cumulant can be written in the form

$$k_n(t) = (2\psi_0)^n \frac{n!}{2}\left\{\frac{1}{n}\int_{-\infty}^{\infty} h^n(u,u)\,du + \frac{1}{\psi_0}\iint_{-\infty}^{\infty} S(t-u)h^n(u,v)S(t-v)\,du\,dv\right\}. \tag{4-72}$$

While this method does not lead to a closed form expression for the frequency function, the cumulants can be computed readily from Eq. (4-72). Thus one at least can obtain sufficiently good approximations to the frequency function through the cumulants. This point is discussed in Chapter 6.

4.8 FILTERED THERMAL NOISE

As an illustrative example of the techniques described, Siegert considered the problem of finding the characteristic function for the process

$$y(t) = \int_0^t x^2(\tau)\,d\tau, \tag{4-73}$$

where $x(t)$ is a Gaussian process.

Siegert [37] chose this example partly because a solution had already been obtained by Rice, [41]. Rice used a simple direct technique to compute the moments of the output signal.

Assume that the covariance function of the input process, $x(t)$, is

$$R(\tau - \eta) = \exp(-|\tau - \eta|), \tag{4-74}$$

with the corresponding spectral density function

$$W(f) = \frac{2}{1+f^2}. \tag{4-75}$$

Insert Eq. (4-75) in the differential equation, Eq. (4-48), which then becomes

(4-76)

$$\left[\frac{d^2}{d\tau^2} - (1 - 4iu)\right]G(\tau,\eta;u) = -2\delta(\tau-\eta); \qquad 0 \le \tau; \qquad \eta \le t.$$

The general solution of this differential equation is

(4-77) $$G(\tau, \eta; u) = A_1(\eta, t; u)e^{-a\tau} + A_2(\tau_2, t; u)e^{a\tau}; \qquad \tau > \eta,$$

and

(4-78) $$G(\tau, \eta; u) = B_1(\eta, t; u)e^{-a\tau} + B_2(\tau_2, t; u)e^{a\tau}; \qquad \tau < \eta,$$

where $a = (1 - 4iu)^{-1/2}$. The coefficients A_1, A_2, B_1, B_2 are related by obtaining the Green's function solution required by the discontinuity at $\tau = \eta$. That is, we must have the function G continuous at $\tau = \eta$ and a jump in its first derivative of value two at this point. These conditions when applied to Eqs. (4-77) and (4-78) give rise to the relations

(4-79) $$B_1 = A_1 - \frac{1}{a} e^{a\eta}$$

$$B_2 = A_2 + \frac{1}{a} e^{-a\eta}.$$

The other conditions which must be satisfied by the coefficients are found by substituting the solutions Eqs. (4-77) and (4-78) into the integral equation for this example which corresponds to Eq. (4-40). For our example the integral equation is

(4-80) $$G(\tau, \eta; u) - 2iu \int_0^t e^{-|\tau_1 - \tau|} G(\tau, \eta; u)\, d\tau_1 = e^{-|\tau - \eta|}.$$

Noting that the coefficients are independent of τ, it is found that

(4-81) $$(1 + a)A_1 + (1 - a)A_2 = \frac{1 + a}{a} e^{a\eta} - \frac{1 - a}{a} e^{-a\eta}$$

and

(4-82) $$(1 - a)e^{-at}A_1 + (1 + a)e^{at}A_2 = 0.$$

Therefore,

(4-83) $$G(\tau, \eta; u) = \frac{(1 + a)e^{a\eta} - (1 - a)e^{-a\eta}}{a[(1 + a)^2 e^{at} - (1 - a)^2 e^{-at}]} [(1 + a)e^{a(t-\tau)} - (1 - a)e^{-a(t-\tau)}],$$

for $\tau > \eta$. If $\tau < \eta$, merely interchange τ and η in Eq. (4-83). Finally apply Eq. (4-41) to get the desired result for the characteristic function:

(4-84)
$$g(u) = \prod_{j=1}^{\infty} (1 - 2iu\lambda_j)^{-1/2} = e^{t/2} \left[\cosh at + \frac{1 + a^2}{2a} \sinh at\right]^{-1/2}.$$

A more realistic example has been computed using these same techniques by Stone, et al. [42]. The important extension is that they have chosen linear filters which are physically realizable in the sense of zero response before zero time.

Let the first filter in Figure 4-2 possess the frequency response function,

$$F_1(\omega) = \left(1 + i\,\frac{\omega - \omega_0}{\omega_1}\right)^{-1} + \left(1 + i\,\frac{\omega + \omega_0}{\omega_1}\right)^{-1}; \qquad \omega_0 = k\omega_1, \qquad k \gg 1. \tag{4-85}$$

The filter following the squarer has the response function

$$F_2(\omega) = \left(1 + i\,\frac{\omega}{\omega_2}\right)^{-1}. \tag{4-86}$$

Under these conditions and a Gaussian input process, the kernel of the homogeneous integral equation, Eq. (4-27), was determined to be

$$k(t - \tau)R(\eta - \tau) \doteq g(x, y) = \frac{2\omega_1^2}{2\gamma - 1}\cos 2k\gamma(x - y)D, \tag{4-87}$$

where

$$\begin{aligned} D &= \exp\,[-2\gamma(x + y)][\exp\,[2(2\gamma - 1)x] - 1], \qquad 0 \le x \le y,\\ D &= \exp\,[-2\gamma(x + y)][\exp\,[2(2\gamma - 1)y] - 1], \qquad 0 \le y \le x, \end{aligned} \tag{4-88}$$

and

$$\gamma = \omega_1/\omega_2. \tag{4-89}$$

For $k\gamma$ large, the system kernel can be expanded in a bilinear series of orthonormal functions,

$$\begin{aligned} h_{nc}(x) &= \frac{2e^{-x}J_{2\gamma-1}(r_n e^{-x})}{J_{2\gamma}(r_n)}\cos 2k\gamma x,\\ h_{ns}(x) &= \frac{2e^{-x}J_{2\gamma-1}(r_n e^{-x})}{J_{2\gamma}(r_n)}\sin 2k\gamma x; \qquad 0 \le x \le \infty\\ J_{2\gamma-1}(r_n) &= 0. \end{aligned} \tag{4-90}$$

The signal was also generalized to consist of noise plus a sinusoid whose *center* frequency was not necessarily restricted to the center frequency ω_0 of the first filter.

Under the assumptions

$$\begin{aligned} &\omega_0 \gg \omega_1,\\ &\alpha = \frac{1}{\omega_1}|\omega - \omega_0| = O(1)\\ &\frac{1}{\omega_1}(\omega + \omega_0) \gg 1, \end{aligned} \tag{4-91}$$

the Laplace transform of the probability frequency function associated with the output of the system takes the form

$$\phi(s, \gamma, y) = \phi(s, \gamma, 0)\exp\left[-y^2\gamma\sum_{k=1}^{\infty}(-1)^{k-1}(8\gamma s)^k B_k(\alpha, \gamma)\right], \tag{4-92}$$

where y is the normalized signal amplitude, $\phi(s, \gamma, 0)$ is the Laplace transform in the absence of the signal (noise only), and

$$B_k(\alpha, \gamma) = \sum_{n=1}^{\infty} \frac{F_{2\gamma-1}^{c^2}(\alpha, r_n) + F_{2\gamma-1}^{s^2}(\alpha, r_n)}{r_n^{2k+4} J_{2\gamma}^2(r_n)}; \qquad k = 1, 2, \ldots \tag{4-93}$$

$$F_{2\gamma-1}^{c,s} = \int_0^\infty dx\, e^{-x} J_{2\gamma-1}(r_n e^{-x}) \begin{cases} \cos 2\gamma\alpha x \\ \sin 2\gamma\alpha x. \end{cases} \tag{4-94}$$

4.9 PRODUCT OF TWO PROCESSES

A related problem to that of squaring and filtering is one in which two separate random processes are multiplied together in a nonlinear device and the output process is passed through a filter, [43, 44, 45].

Consider the transformation of an input process $x(t)$ by a general nonlinear device having zero memory and which can be characterized by the relation

$$y(t) = \int_0^\infty K[x(t - \tau), \tau]\, d\tau, \tag{4-95}$$

where $K(u, v)$ is a real-valued function of its arguments satisfying the one-sided homogeneity condition

$$K(\lambda u, v) = \lambda^\nu K(u, v) \tag{4-96}$$

for all $\lambda > 0$ and some real ν.

After each of two random processes have been transformed by similar devices having the above characteristics, we wish to determine the cross-correlation function

$$\begin{aligned} \psi &= E\{y_1(t) y_2(t + \sigma)\} \\ &= E\left\{\iint_0^\infty K[x_1(t - \xi, \xi)] K[x_2(t + \tau - \eta)]\, d\xi\, d\eta\right\}. \end{aligned} \tag{4-97}$$

Let x_1 and x_2 have the joint Gaussian frequency function $f(x_1, x_2, \overline{x_1^2}, \overline{x_2^2}; \rho)$ where $E\{x_i^2\} = \overline{x_i^2}$ and $\rho = E\{x_1(t) x_2(t + \tau)\}$.
Then Eq. (4-97) becomes

$$\psi = \int_{-\infty}^{\infty} \int_{-\infty}^{\infty} d\tau\, d\eta \int_{-\infty}^{\infty} \int_{-\infty}^{\infty} K(x_1, \xi) K(x_2, \eta) \; f[x_1, x_2, \overline{x_1^2}, \overline{x_2^2}, \rho(\tau - \eta + \xi)]\, dx_1\, dx_2. \tag{4-98}$$

The frequency function can be put into a normalized form by making the following changes in variable

(4-99)
$$x = x_1/(\overline{x_1^2})^{1/2}$$
$$y = x_2/(\overline{x_2^2})^{1/2}$$
$$h(\tau) = \frac{g(\tau)}{(\overline{x_1^2 x_2^2})^{1/2}}.$$

When these changes are made and the homogeneity condition is used, Eq. (4-98) becomes

(4-100)
$$\psi(\tau) = (\overline{x_1^2 x_2^2})^{\nu/2} \int_0^\infty \int_0^\infty \left\{ \int_{-\infty}^\infty \int_{-\infty}^\infty K(x, \xi) K(y, \eta) \right.$$
$$\left. f[x, y, h(\tau - \eta + \xi)]\, dx\, dy \right\} d\xi\, d\eta.$$

Define $\phi_\rho(\sigma, \tau)$ to be the output correlation function of a device $K(x, y)$ when the input is a stationary Gaussian process with mean zero and variance σ^2; having a normalized correlation coefficient $\rho(\tau)$. Under these conditions the right hand side of (4-100) is simply $\phi_h(1, \tau)$. Therefore

(4-101)
$$\psi(\tau) = (\overline{x_1^2 x_2^2})^{\nu/2} \phi_h(1, \tau).$$

This is the main result obtained by Brown and easily reduces to the form given in [44].

Two explicit statements are contained in Eq. (4-101) which will be proven in another fashion and elaborated on in Chapter 5. These are:

(i) The square law detector is equivalent to a zero memory square law transformation followed by a low pass linear filter.
(ii) An envelope detector is equivalent to a half-wave linear transformation followed by a low pass linear filter.

Roe and White, [45], have considered a similar situation but have generalized the problem to include a signal plus noise as the input to each channel. A summary follows of their development for the characteristic function of the process obtained after multiplication of two signals, each perturbed by additive Gaussian processes. The general problem is to evaluate

(4-102)
$$\beta(\tau) = \frac{1}{2W} \int_0^T x(t) y(t + \tau)\, dt,$$

where $x(t)$ and $y(t)$ are assumed to be bandwidth limited functions of width $-W$ to $+W$. Under these conditions the integral can be approximated by the finite series

(4-103)
$$\beta = \sum_{j=1}^{k} X_j Y_j,$$

where X_j, Y_j are k samples taken at the Nyquist intervals corresponding to T and W (re. Chapter 8).

The general case considered can be written as

$$(4\text{-}104) \qquad \beta = \sum_{j=1}^{k} X_j Y_j = \sum_{j=1}^{k} (As_{j,x} + N_{j,x})(Bs_{j,y} + N_{j,y}).$$

The noise signals are zero mean Gaussian processes for which

$$(4\text{-}105) \qquad \begin{aligned} E\{N_{j,x}N_{m,x}\} &= \sigma_x^2\,\delta_{jm}, \qquad \text{Kronecker-delta} \\ E\{N_{j,y}N_{m,y}\} &= \sigma_y^2\,\delta_{jm} \\ E\{N_{j,x}N_{m,y}\} &= \rho\sigma_x\sigma_y\,\delta_{jm}. \end{aligned}$$

If the signals are the same in each channel, then $\rho = 0$, $s_{j,x} = s_{j,y}$, $A = B = 1$. If one channel is to contain signal plus noise and the other only noise; $\rho = 0$, $A = 1$, $B = 0$.

It is convenient to proceed with the normalized quantities

$$(4\text{-}106) \qquad \begin{aligned} \psi &= \beta/\sigma^2 \\ \sigma^2 &= \sigma_x\sigma_y. \end{aligned}$$

Adjust the coefficient B in Eq. (4-104) so that

$$(4\text{-}107) \qquad \sum_{j=1}^{k} s_{j,x}^2 = \sum_{j=1}^{k} s_{j,y}^2.$$

The measure of the signal-to-noise ratio is defined as

$$(4\text{-}108) \qquad R = \frac{1}{\sigma^2}\sum_{j=1}^{k} s_{j,x}^2 = \frac{1}{\sigma^2}\sum_{j=1}^{k} s_{j,y}^2,$$

where Eq. (4-107) is assumed to be satisfied.

The problem is to compute the probability function of ψ. Again, as in many instances, we will have to be content with obtaining the characteristic function. We start with the joint frequency function of the variables

$$(4\text{-}109) \qquad \begin{aligned} x_j &= \frac{X_j}{\sigma_x} = \frac{As_{j,x}}{\sigma_x} + \frac{N_{j,x}}{\sigma_x} = as_{j,x} + n_{j,x} \\ y_j &= \frac{Y_j}{\sigma_y} = \frac{Bs_{j,y}}{\sigma_y} + \frac{N_{j,y}}{\sigma_y} = bs_{j,y} + n_{j,y}. \end{aligned}$$

The joint function, therefore, is

$$(4\text{-}110) \qquad f(x_j, y_j) = \frac{1}{2\pi(1-\rho^2)^{1/2}} \exp\left[-\frac{1}{2(1-\rho^2)}\{(x_j - as_{j,x})^2 - 2\rho(x_j - as_{j,x})(y_j - bs_{j,y}) + (y_j - bs_{j,y})^2\}\right].$$

Make the change of variable $\psi_j = x_j y_j$. Since the Jacobian of the transformation is $\left|\frac{1}{x_j}\right|$, the transformed frequency function is

$$f(x_j, \psi_j) = \frac{1}{2\pi|x_j|(1-\rho^2)^{1/2}} \exp\left[-\frac{1}{2(1-\rho^2)}\left\{(x_j - as_{j,x})^2 - 2\rho(x_j - as_{j,x})\left(\frac{\psi_j}{x_j} - bs_{j,y}\right) + \left(\frac{\psi_j}{x_j} - bs_{j,y}\right)^2\right\}\right]. \tag{4-111}$$

The Fourier transform relative to ψ_i is

$$F(x_j, u_j) = \int_{-\infty}^{\infty} f(x_j, \psi_j) \exp(iu_j\psi_j)\, d\psi_j. \tag{4-112}$$

Insert Eq. (4-111) and integrate with respect to ψ_j. Then compute

$$\begin{aligned} F(u_j) &= \int_{-\infty}^{\infty} F(x_j, u_j)\, dx_j \\ &= \frac{1}{[1 - 2iu_j\rho + u_j^2(1-\rho^2)]^{1/2}} \\ &\quad \cdot \exp\left\{\frac{2iu_jabs_{j,x}s_{j,y} - u_i^2[b^2s_{j,y}^2 - 2\rho abs_{j,x}s_{j,y} + a^2s_{j,x}^2]}{2[1 - 2iu_j\rho + u_j^2(1-\rho^2)]}\right\}. \end{aligned} \tag{4-113}$$

Since the samples were chosen at Nyquist intervals, the ψ_i are independent and the characteristic function for the sum

$$\psi = \sum_{j=1}^{k} \psi_j \tag{4-114}$$

is the product of the k characteristic functions $F(u_j)$.

The final result, with appropriate new definitions, can be written in the form

$$f(\psi) = \frac{1}{2\pi}\int_{-\infty}^{\infty} F(u)\, e^{-iu\psi}\, du \tag{4-115}$$

$$= \frac{L(\psi, \rho)}{2\pi}\int_{-\infty}^{\infty} \frac{1}{(1+z^2)^{k/2}} \exp\left\{-\frac{R(hz^2 - izC)}{(1-\rho^2)(1+z^2)}\right\} \exp\left\{-\frac{iz\psi}{1-\rho^2}\right\} dz,$$

where

$$L = L(\psi, \rho) = (1-\rho^2)^{k/2-1} \exp\left\{\frac{\rho}{1-\rho^2}\left[\psi - R\sigma^2\left(abr - \frac{\rho}{2}(a^2+b^2)\right)\right]\right\} \tag{4-116}$$

$$\begin{aligned} C &= \sigma^2\,[abr(1+\rho^2) - \rho\,(a^2+b^2)] \\ &= ABr\,(1+\rho^2) - \rho\left(\frac{A^2\sigma^2}{\sigma_x^2} + \frac{B^2\sigma^2}{\sigma_y^2}\right), \end{aligned} \tag{4-117}$$

$$\begin{aligned} h &= \sigma^2\,[\tfrac{1}{2}(a^2+b^2)\,(1+\rho^2) - 2\rho abr] \\ &= \frac{\sigma^2}{2}\left(\frac{A^2}{\sigma_x^2} + \frac{B^2}{\sigma_y^2}\right)(1+\rho^2) - 2\rho ABr, \end{aligned} \tag{4-118}$$

$$r = \sum_{j=1}^{k} s_{j,x}\, s_{j,y} \Big/ \sum_{j=1}^{k} s_{j,x}^2. \tag{4-119}$$

Because of the generality of Eq. (4-115), it is not at all surprising that this result includes several already known solutions of similar noise theory problems, [45].

It should be remarked that the techniques used by Kac, Siegert and Emerson relied upon a series representation in which the orthonormal functions were eigenfunctions of a certain homogeneous integral equation. Roe and White rely on sampling the processes at Nyquist intervals to obtain samples which are stochastically independent and thereby permit a series representation of the system integration equation.

5 MODULATION AND DETECTION

5.1 SIMPLE DETECTION MODEL

Modulators and detectors occur so often as elements of physical systems that a detailed study of this class of nonlinear devices is justified. The reader may notice that several of the results developed in this chapter are merely special cases of more general relations already discussed. The reason for repeating is to illustrate alternative analytical approaches which have been tailored to handle modulators and detectors.

First, let us dispose of the names *modulator* and *detector*. Mathematically, as will be shown, these are the same generic nonlinear device; the differences occurring only insofar as to decide which portion of the output spectrum of the transformed process will be retained and called the *desired signal*. Usually, but not necessarily always, the detector is the transformation for which the low frequency spectral terms are retained, while the modulator is the transformation for which some specified portion of the higher frequency spectral terms are retained. With this interpretation, the generic term *detector* will be used throughout with no regard concerning which portion of the output spectrum is to be considered as the signal.

Some of the basic concepts of detector terminology can be examined by considering the simple circuit of Figure 5-1. The simple *schoolboy* theory of detection will be reproduced to illustrate some basic notions.

Let the input signals, E_1 and E_2 be simple sinusoids of the form

$$E_1(t) = A_1 \cos 2\pi f_1 t \qquad (5\text{-}1)$$

$$E_2(t) = A_2 \cos 2\pi f_2 t.$$

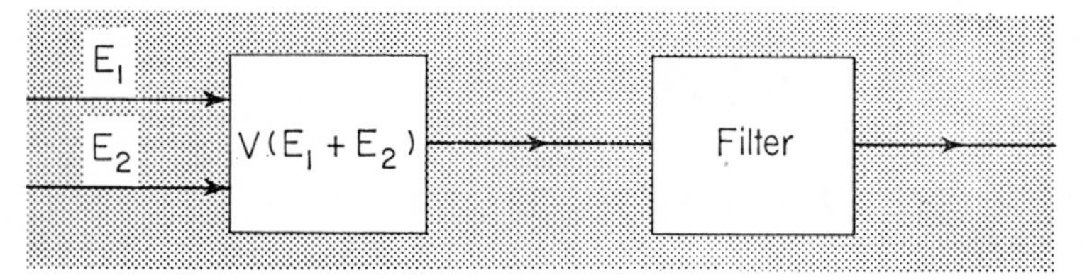

Figure 5-1. Basic Detector

The nonlinear transformation $V(E)$ is represented by the linear and quadratic terms of a power series expansion. For the given example,

(5-2)

$$
\begin{aligned}
V[E_1 + E_2] &= B_2(E_1 + E_2)^2 + B_1(E_1 + E_2) \\
&= [A_1^2 \cos^2 2\pi f_1 t + A_2^2 \cos 2\pi f_2 t + 2A_1A_2 \cos 2\pi f_1 t \cos 2\pi f_2 t_1]B_2 \\
&\quad + B_1[A_1 \cos 2\pi f_1 t + A_2 \cos 2\pi f_2 t].
\end{aligned}
$$

The detector action can be seen after making trigonometrical transformations in Eq. (5-2). One can show that

(5-3)

$$
\begin{aligned}
V[E_1 + E_2] &= B_1[A_1 \cos 2\pi f_1 t + A_2 \cos 2\pi f_2 t] \\
&\quad + B_2\left[\frac{A_1^2 + A_2^2}{2}\right] + \frac{B_2}{2}[A_1^2 \cos 4\pi f_1 t + A_2^2 \cos 4\pi f_2 t] \\
&\quad + B_2A_1A_2[\cos 2\pi(f_1 - f_2)t + \cos 2\pi(f_1 + f_2)t].
\end{aligned}
$$

This expression illustrates the basic actions performed by a detector. The first term indicates that the original two frequency terms appear in the output modified by an amplitude change of B_1. The second term is a constant and is called the zero frequency or dc term (direct current). The third term contains twice the original frequencies and is usually part of the output which is classed as the *higher frequency terms*. Three specific names are attached to the detector in its generic form when only selected terms are retained after passing the detector output through a linear filter. These are

(a) Detector: zero frequency terms
(b) Modulator: sum or difference frequencies
(c) Multiplier: higher order terms.

The next few sections will deal with more generalized detector characteristics. To avoid mathematical manipulation difficulties, the input signals to the detectors will always be assumed to be narrow band Gaussian processes. Thus the basic analytical techniques can be presented without the complications that can arise when a signal is added to the noise. The treatment of detection for signal plus noise in specific cases has been treated by several authors, [46, 47, 48].

5.2 SIMPLE DETECTORS

Four detector types have been chosen as examples illustrating some analytical techniques applicable to situations in which detectors are employed.

These are

(a) linear detector
(b) envelope detector
(c) square law detector
(d) $\nu'th$ law detector.

Three types of correlation functions occur in the development of the detector theory. The reader is cautioned that care must be exercised in using the results to be certain just what correlation function appears in a given expression.

5.2.1 LINEAR DETECTOR

The linear detector is defined as a simple half-wave rectifier operating with the characteristic

$$x(t) = \alpha y(t); \qquad y \geq 0$$
$$= 0 \quad ; \qquad y < 0. \tag{5-4}$$

A full wave rectifier characteristic could be used also, but little change is required in the results. In Chapter 2, Eq. (2-62), the output correlation function for the half-wave rectifier was found to be

$$\psi(\tau) = \frac{\alpha^2 R_\tau}{4} + \frac{\alpha^2 R_0}{2\pi}\, {}_2F_1\left(-\frac{1}{2}, -\frac{1}{2}; \frac{1}{2}; \frac{R_\tau^2}{R_0^2}\right), \tag{5-5}$$

where

$$R_\tau = E\{y(t)y(t+\tau)\}$$
$$R_0 = E\{y^2(t)\}. \tag{5-6}$$

Equation (5-5) is completely general in the sense of Eq. (5-3). That is, it contains all the spectral frequencies that arise from half-wave rectification of the input Gaussian process $y(t)$. Suppose we concern ourselves only with the low-frequency, or video, components of the detector output, i.e., the spectrum resulting from passing the rectifier output through an isolated low-pass filter.

One direct approach to obtain the resulting spectrum is first to apply the transform theorem to obtain the power density spectrum from the correlation function of the rectified output signal, Eq. (5-5). The spectral components are then multiplied by the power frequency response of the low-pass filter and the result is subjected to a Fourier transform to obtain the video correlation function. Application of this *brute-force* method immediately shows that the term $\alpha^2 R_\tau/4$ should be deleted because it corresponds to the original frequency terms.

Instead of using the direct method, an alternative scheme will be applied which easily modifies Eq. (5-5) to give the desired output correlation function.

The original input random process can be represented by the series

(5-7) $$y(t) = \sum_{n=1}^{N} C_n \cos(\omega_n t - \theta_n),$$

where the phase angles θ_n are uniformly distributed in the range $(0, 2\pi)$. The input correlation function to the rectifier is

(5-8) $$R_\tau = E\{y(t)y(t-\tau)\} = \tfrac{1}{2}\sum_{n=1}^{N} C_n^2 \cos \omega_n \tau.$$

Using the methods of Chapter 1, we can write $Z(\tau)$ the pre-envelope function of R_τ as

(5-9) $$Z(\tau) = R_\tau + i\hat{R}_\tau = \frac{1}{2}\sum_n C_n^2 \cos \omega_n \tau + \frac{i}{2}\sum_n C_n^2 \sin \omega_n \tau.$$

Select some arbitrary frequency Ω and write

(5-10)

$$Z(\tau) = \frac{1}{2}\sum_n C_n^2 \cos[(\omega_n - \Omega)t + \Omega t] + \frac{i}{2}\sum_n C_n^2 \sin[(\omega_n - \Omega)t + \Omega t],$$

or

(5-11) $$Z(\tau) = [\mu_{13}(\tau) + i\mu_{14}(\tau)]e^{i\Omega\tau},$$

where

(5-12) $$\mu_{13}(\tau) = \tfrac{1}{2}\sum_{n=1}^{N} C_n^2 \cos(\omega_n - \Omega)\tau$$

and

(5-13) $$\mu_{14}(\tau) = \tfrac{1}{2}\sum_{n=1}^{N} C_n^2 \sin(\omega_n - \Omega)\tau.$$

Putting this together, write

(5-14) $$\frac{R_\tau}{R_0} = \frac{[\mu_{13}^2 + \mu_{14}^2]^{1/2}}{R_0}\cos[\Omega\tau + \Phi(\tau)] = \rho(\tau)\cos[\Omega\tau + \Phi(\tau)],$$

where

$$\Phi(\tau) = \tan^{-1} - \frac{\mu_{14}}{\mu_{13}}. \tag{5-15}$$

ρ is the envelope of the normalized input process's correlation function. It will now be demonstrated that $\rho(\tau)$ is the appropriate correlation function to use in Eq. (5-5) when only the low frequency spectral terms are desired from the output of the detector-low-pass-filter combination.

Notice that the quantity R_τ/R_0 always occurs in even powers in the hypergeometric series of Eq. (5-5). Consider the Fourier transform of a general term of this series. Neglecting numerical constants, we have

$$\mathfrak{F}\left\{\left(\frac{R_\tau}{R_0}\right)^{2n}\right\} = \mathfrak{F}\,\{\rho^{2n}(\tau)\cos^{2n}[\Omega\tau + \phi(\tau)]\}. \tag{5-16}$$

Expand the trigonometric term into its series representation:

(5-17)

$$\cos^{2k} x = \frac{1}{2^{2k-1}}\left[\cos 2kx + 2k\cos 2(k-1)x + \frac{(2k)(2k-1)}{2!}\cos 2(k-2)x + \dots + \frac{(2k)!}{(k-1)!\,(k+1)!}\cos 2x + \frac{(2k)!}{k!k!2}\right].$$

Write the transform of a typical term of the right-hand side of Eq. (5-16) after Eq. (5-17) has been inserted. For example

$$W'_{2n}(f) = 4\int_0^\infty \rho^{2n}(\tau)\cos h(n)\,[\Omega\tau + \Phi(\tau)]\cos 2\pi f\tau\, d\tau, \tag{5-18}$$

where $h(n)$ symbolizes a polynomial in n. By a trigonometrical expansion,

$$W'_{2n}(f) = 4\int_0^\infty \rho^{2n}(\tau)\cos 2\pi\tau[h(n)f_\Omega \pm f]\cos h(n)\Phi(\tau) - \sin 2\pi\tau[h(n)f_\Omega \pm f]\sin h(n)\Phi(\tau)\, d\tau. \tag{5-19}$$

Each such typical term will evidently correspond to frequencies $h(n)\dfrac{\Omega}{2\pi} \pm f$. These spectral contributions would be eliminated by the low-pass filter because by assumption $\Omega/2\pi$ is large compared to any desired video frequency, f. Therefore, the conclusion is that only the constant last term of the series in Eq. (5-17), will lead to a low frequency spectral component in the output signal. Keeping only these terms is exactly equivalent to replacing $(R_\tau/R_0)^{2n}$ by the input envelope correlation term $\rho^{2n}(\tau)$ and multiplying by a constant depending on $2n$. When one applies this reasoning to Eq. (5-5), the result for the low frequency output correlation function is

$$\psi_v(\tau) = \frac{\alpha^2 R_0}{2\pi}\sum_{n=1}^{\infty}\frac{(-\frac{1}{2})_n(-\frac{1}{2})_n}{(\frac{1}{2})_n}\,\frac{(2n)!}{n!n!2^{2n}}\,\frac{\rho^{2n}}{n!}. \tag{5-20}$$

Insert the identity, (appendix)

$$\left(\frac{1}{2}\right)_n = \frac{(2n)!}{2^{2n}n!}, \tag{5-21}$$

to obtain

$$\psi_v(\tau) = \frac{\alpha^2 R_0}{2\pi} \sum_{n=0}^{\infty} \frac{(-\frac{1}{2})_n(-\frac{1}{2})_n}{n!n!} \rho^{2n}, \tag{5-22}$$

or

$$\psi_v(\tau) = \frac{\alpha^2 R_0}{2\pi} F\left(-\frac{1}{2}, -\frac{1}{2}; 1; \rho^2\right). \tag{5-23}$$

The normalizing constant is

$$\psi_v(0) = \frac{\alpha^2 R_0}{2\pi} F\left(-\frac{1}{2}, -\frac{1}{2}; 1; 1\right) \tag{5-24}$$

$$= \frac{\alpha^2 R_0}{2\pi} \cdot \frac{4}{\pi}.$$

Hence,

$$\frac{\psi_v(\tau)}{\psi_v(0)} = \frac{\pi}{4} F\left(-\frac{1}{2}, -\frac{1}{2}; 1; \rho^2\right). \tag{5-25}$$

Notice that Eq. (5-25) corresponds exactly to Eq. (3-11) which was derived as the correlation function for the output of a linear envelope detector. Essentially, we have given a heuristic proof for the commonly accepted fact that a linear envelope detector is equivalent to a linear half-wave detector, followed by a low pass filter. The proof is not complete because it has only been shown that the two output correlation functions are the same. A complete proof would have to show that the output signal statistics were the same.

5.2.2 SQUARE-LAW DETECTOR

The square law detector is defined by the characteristic

$$x(t) = \alpha y^2(t). \tag{5-26}$$

This is nothing more than the squarer discussed in Chapter 4. However, we will obtain some further results by applying the characteristic function method of Chapter 2. Referring to Table 2-1, the appropriate system function is

$$F(iu) = \int_0^\infty x(y) e^{-iuy}\, dy = \frac{2\alpha}{iu^3}. \tag{5-27}$$

The contour of integration, c, will be a positive loop about the origin. The output correlation function is computed from Eq. (2-6), using the joint characteristic function for an input Gaussian process, $y(t)$. Thus we have

$$\psi(\tau) = \frac{-4\alpha^2}{4\pi^2} \int_c \frac{1}{u^3}\, du \int_c \frac{dv}{v^2} \exp\left\{-\frac{1}{2}\left[R_0 u^2 + R_0 v^2 + 2R_\tau uv\right]\right\}. \tag{5-28}$$

Expand the cross-product term into its series form:

$$\psi(\tau) = \frac{-\alpha^2}{\pi^2} \sum_{q=0}^{\infty} \frac{(-1)^q R_\tau^q}{q!} \left(\int_c u^{q-3} e^{-R_0 u^2/2} \, du \right)^2. \tag{5-29}$$

Again, expand the remaining exponential function to obtain the form

$$\psi(\tau) = \frac{-\alpha^2}{\pi^2} \sum_{q=0}^{\infty} \frac{(-1)^q R_\tau^q}{q!} \left[\sum_{n=0}^{\infty} \frac{\left(-\frac{R_0}{2}\right)^n}{n!} \int_c u^{q-3+2n} \, du \right]^2. \tag{5-30}$$

The remaining integral vanishes except for the residues which occur at $(q = 0, n = 1)$ and $(q = 2, n = 0)$. The residues at these points are:

$$(q = 0, n = 1) \text{ residue } = -\frac{R_0}{2}$$

$$(q = 2, n = 0) \text{ residue } = -\frac{R_\tau^2}{2}.$$

Placing these residues in Eq. (5-30) produces

$$\psi(\tau) = \alpha^2 R_0^2 \left[1 + 2 \left(\frac{R_\tau}{R_0} \right)^2 \right]. \tag{5-31}$$

If only the low frequency terms are of interest, the same arguments used for the linear detector can be applied. One finds that the low frequency terms correspond to the result of replacing

$$\left(\frac{R_\tau}{R_0} \right)^2 \text{ by } \frac{(2n)!}{n!n!2^{2n}} \rho^{2n} \text{ for the only significant}$$

value $n = 1$.

The net result is

$$\psi_s(\tau) = \alpha^2 R_0^2 (1 + \rho^2), \tag{5-32}$$

which when normalized, becomes

$$\frac{\psi_s(\tau)}{\psi_s(0)} = \frac{1 + \rho^2}{2}. \tag{5-33}$$

Notice that Eq. (5-33) corresponds to Eq. (3-28), which is the correlation function for the squared envelope detector.

5.2.3 *ν'th LAW DETECTOR*

As a preliminary to the next section, the correlation function will be formulated for the low frequency output signal transformed by a *ν'th* law detector acting upon a Gaussian process. The *ν'th* law detector is not a very useful device in itself. It is most important as an analytical tool to answer questions as to what occurs in a physical system if the detector is not truly linear, square law, or any assumed power law. Define the ν'*th* law detector by the transformation

$$x(t) = \alpha y^{\nu}(t); \qquad y \geq 0 \tag{5-34}$$
$$x(t) = 0 \quad ; \qquad y < 0,$$

where ν = any positive number, not necessarily an integer.

We will again employ the characteristic function method. In Table 2-1, the system function is listed as

$$F(iu) = \frac{\alpha\Gamma(v+1)}{(iu)^{\nu+1}}. \tag{5-35}$$

In deriving the basic equation in Chapter 2 for the characteristic function method, certain liberties were taken with complex numbers which until now were of little importance. Equation (2-6) is more precisely written as

$$\psi(\tau) = \frac{1}{4\pi^2}\int_c\int_c F(ue^{i\pi})F(ve^{i\pi})g(u, v; \tau)\,du\,dv. \tag{5-36}$$

The general joint characteristic function for two variates is

$$g(u, v; \tau) = \exp\left[-\tfrac{1}{2}(\sigma_{22}u^2 + \sigma_{11}v^2 + 2\sigma_{12}uv)\right]. \tag{5-37}$$

This general form of $g(u, v; \tau)$ is required as a preliminary development for the following section. Combine Eqs. (5-36) and (5-37). Expand the exponential containing the cross-product term to obtain

$$\psi(\tau) = \alpha^2\Gamma^2(\nu+1)\sum_{n=0}^{\infty}\frac{(-1)^n\sigma_{12}^n}{n!}\int_c\frac{u^{n-\nu-1}}{\exp\left[i\frac{\pi}{2}(\nu+1)\right]}\exp\left[-\frac{\sigma_{22}}{u}\right]du\int_c\frac{v^{n-\nu-1}}{\exp\left[i\frac{\pi}{2}(\nu+1)\right]}\exp\left[-\frac{\sigma_{11}}{2}v^2\right]dv. \tag{5-38}$$

The contour of integration is along the real axis with a downward indentation at the origin. If ν is not an integer, there is no pole at the origin. For the value $\nu = 1$, the device degenerates to a linear detector. In this case it has already been shown that a pole at $\nu = 1$ gives rise to an output signal containing the original input frequencies. It is assumed that these original frequency components are eliminated by isolated linear filters following the detector. Thus we can pass over the case in which $\nu = 1$ has a pole at the origin. The same situation occurs when $\nu = 2$. Higher integral values are of little practical interest, but if one desires the same techniques can be used to discuss the frequency terms corresponding to poles at the origin.

Consider one of the contour integrals in Eq. (5-38). Since we have decided to neglect the contributions at possible poles

(5-39) $$I = \int_c \frac{u^{n-\nu-1}}{\exp\left[i\frac{\pi}{2}(\nu+1)\right]} \exp\left[-\frac{\sigma_{22}u^2}{2}\right] du,$$

$$I = \exp\left[-i\frac{\pi}{2}(\nu+1)\right] \int_{-\infty}^{0} u^{n-\nu-1} \exp\left[-\frac{\sigma_{22}u^2}{2}\right] du$$

$$+ \exp\left[-i\frac{\pi}{2}(\nu+1)\right] \int_{0}^{\infty} u^{n-\nu-1} \exp\left[-\frac{\sigma_{22}u^2}{2}\right] du,$$

$$I = e^{-in\pi} \exp\left[i\frac{\pi}{2}(\nu+1)\right] \int_{0}^{\infty} u^{n-\nu-1} \exp\left[-\frac{\sigma_{22}u^2}{2}\right] du$$

$$+ \exp\left[-i\frac{\pi}{2}(\nu+1)\right] \int_{0}^{\infty} u^{n-\nu-1} \exp\left[-\frac{\sigma_{22}u^2}{2}\right] du.$$

After a little manipulation we find that

(5-40) $$I = \left\{[(-1)^n + 1] \cos\frac{\pi}{2}(\nu+1) + i[(-1)^n - 1] \sin\frac{\pi}{2}(\nu+1)\right\} \left(\frac{2}{\sigma_{22}}\right)^{(n-\nu)/2} \Gamma\left(\frac{n-\nu}{2}\right).$$

Substitute Eq. (5-40) in Eq. (5-38);

(5-41) $$\psi(\tau) = \frac{\alpha^2\Gamma^2(\nu+1)}{\pi^2 2^{\nu+2}} (\sigma_{11}\sigma_{22})^{\nu/2} \sum_{n=0}^{\infty} \frac{(-1)^n \sigma_{12}^n \Gamma^2 \dfrac{(n-\nu)}{2} 2^n}{(\sigma_{11}\sigma_{22})^{n/2} n!}$$

$$\cdot\left\{[(-1)^n + 1]^2 \cos^2\frac{\pi}{2}(\nu+1) - [(-1)^n - 1]^2 \sin^2\frac{\pi}{2}(\nu+1)\right\}.$$

Let σ_{12e} denote the envelope of the correlation function σ_{12}. Then if one applies exactly the same arguments used to reduce the correlation function of the linear detector to low frequency spectral terms, it follows that if only the low frequency terms are desired Eq. (5-41) becomes

(5-42) $$\psi_\nu(\tau) = \frac{\alpha^2\Gamma^2(\nu+1)}{\pi^2 2^{\nu+2}} 4\cos^2\frac{\pi}{2}(\nu+1) \cdot (\sigma_{11}\sigma_{22})^{\nu/2}$$

$$\cdot \sum_{n=0}^{\infty} \frac{\Gamma^2\left(\dfrac{2n-\nu}{2}\right)(2n)!2^{2n}}{(2n)!2^{2n}n!n!} \left(\frac{\sigma_{12e}^2}{\sigma_{11}\sigma_{22}}\right)^n,$$

which can be written in the hypergeometric form

(5-43) $$\psi_\nu(\tau) = Q(\nu)\,(\sigma_{11}\sigma_{22})^{\nu/2}\,{}_2F_1\left(-\nu/2, -\nu/2; 1; \frac{\sigma_{12e}^2}{\sigma_{11}\sigma_{22}}\right).$$

Q_ν is defined by identification of terms between Eq. (5-43) and (5-42). If one lets $\nu = 1$, Eq. (5-43) reduces to Eq. (5-23) for the linear detector and if $\nu = 2$, Eq. (5-43) reduces to Eq. (5-32) for the square law detector.

5.3 DETECTION OF THE SUM OF RANDOM PROCESSES

There are many instances in modern communication systems wherein the signal has the statistical properties of a bandwidth limited random process. Particularly interesting results occur when two or more modulated noise-like signals are added together to serve as the input signal to a *ν'th* law detector, [49, 50]. These results are of sufficient practical significance to justify their presentation; however, it is the technique itself which will be our primary interest. For the first time in this book we will have to deal with a random process which is not truly stationary.

The input signals will have all the characteristics of real Gaussian random processes but in addition will have certain regularities introduced by modulating the random processes. These signals will be of the form $M(t)\,x(t)$, where $x(t)$ is a Gaussian process and $M(t)$ can be a general piecewise continuous real time function.

The analysis technique is to define the problem in such a way that the correlation function found in Eq. (5-43) is applicable. Let the input signal be taken as the sum of two modulated processes. That is,

$$x_1 = x(t) = M_1(t)y_1(t) + M_2(t)y_2(t) \tag{5-44}$$

and

$$x_2 = x(t+\tau) = M_1(t+\tau)y_1(t+\tau) + M_2(t+\tau)y_2(t+\tau).$$

Assume that $y_1(t)$ and $y_2(t)$ are jointly Gaussian distributed. This implies that $y_1(t+\tau)$ and $y_2(t+\tau)$ will be so jointly distributed.

From Eq. (5-44), the second moments, or powers are consequently

$$\begin{aligned} \sigma_{11} &= E\{x_1^2\} = M_1^2(t)R_{01} + M_2^2(t)R_{02} \\ \sigma_{22} &= E\{x_2^2\} = M_1^2(t+\tau)R_{01} + M_2^2(t+\tau)R_{02}. \end{aligned} \tag{5-45}$$

The correlation function of the combined input signal is

$$\sigma_{12} = E\{x_1x_2\} = M_1(t)M_1(t+\tau)R_{\tau 1} + M_2(t)M_2(t+\tau)R_{\tau 2}; \tag{5-46}$$

where $R_{\tau i}$ is the correlation function of the original unmodulated processes. σ_{12e} will designate the envelope of the correlation function σ_{12}.

Because we are now dealing with a quasi-stationary process, Eq. (5-43) must be modified by taking a time average because strictly speaking in place of Eq. (5-46) we require

$$\sigma_{12}^* = \langle E\{x_1x_2\}\rangle, \tag{5-47}$$

where $\langle\cdot\rangle$ denotes a temporal average. With this in mind, the output correlation function corresponding to the low frequency terms is

$$\psi_\nu(\tau) = \left\langle Q(\nu)\,(\sigma_{11}\sigma_{22})^{\nu/2}\,{}_2F_1\left(-\nu/2,\,-\nu/2;\,1;\,\frac{\sigma_{12e}^2}{\sigma_{11}\sigma_{22}}\right)\right\rangle. \tag{5-48}$$

In order to exhibit some explicit results, let the modulating functions be the simple form most often used in modulation theory.
That is, let

(5-49)
$$M_1(t) = 1 + m_1 \cos \omega_1 t$$
$$M_2(t) = 1 + m_2 \cos (\omega_2 t + \theta).$$

The constants m_i are called the *modulation* indices. θ is an arbitrary phase angle. Even with the simple form of Eq. (5-49), it is impossible to evaluate Eq. (5-48) in *closed form* for arbitrary values of the signal constants. Further progress requires discussion of limiting cases.

5.3.1 CASE A: $M_1(t)R_{01} \gg M_2(t)R_{02}$.

The discontinuous portion of the output spectrum (spikes at discrete frequencies) will correspond to the first term of the series development of Eq. (5-48). Denote this term by ψ_{DC}, then

(5-50)
$$\psi_{\nu DC} = \langle Q(\nu)(\sigma_{11}\sigma_{22})^{\nu/2}\rangle.$$

Substituting the defined quantities with the given magnitude restriction produces

(5-51)
$$\psi_{\nu DC} \approx Q(\nu)[M_1^2(t)M_1^2(t+\tau)R_{01}]^{\nu/2}.$$

Without evaluating the Fourier transform of the $\psi_{\nu DC}$, it is apparent that the low frequency spectral spikes are governed only by the stronger of the two signals. Thus a complete suppression of the weaker by the stronger signal occurs in the ν'*th* law device at low frequencies.

5.3.2 CASE B: SMALL MODULATION INDICES

Consider the case of arbitrary signal strengths R_{oi}, but with modulation indices sufficiently small so that

(5-52)
$$m_i^2 \ll m_i; \qquad i = 1, 2.$$

The first term of Eq. (5-48) will again correspond to spectral spikes exhibiting the same general suppression effects encountered in Case A. The second term is of considerable interest and after consolidation of constants can be written as

(5-53)
$$\psi_{\nu 2}(\tau) = \left\langle Q_1(\nu)\frac{\sigma_{12e}^2}{\sigma_{11}\sigma_{22}}\right\rangle.$$

Substitute the definitions of Eqs. (5-45), (5-46) and (5-47) into Eq. (5-53).

(5-54)
$$\psi_{\nu 2}(\tau) =$$
$$\left\langle Q_1(\tau)\left\{\frac{[M_1(t)M_1(t+\tau)R_{\tau 1} + M_2(t)M_2(t+\tau)R_{\tau 2}]^2}{\{[M_1^2(t)R_{01} + M_2^2(t)R_{02}][M_1^2(t+\tau)R_{01} + M_2^2(t+\tau)R_{02}]\}^{1-\nu/2}}\right\}\right\rangle.$$

If the frequency spectrum of the two unmodulated input processes are centered at different frequencies, the cross-product term in the numerator of Eq. (5-54) will correspond to the difference frequency terms in the output signal.

For definiteness, let $\theta = \pi$ in Eq. (5-49). We will focus our attention on the cross-product term whose time average will be designated by $\psi_3(\tau)$. Thus

(5-55)

$$\psi_3(\tau, t) = 2Q_1(\nu) \frac{R_{\tau 1}R_{\tau 2}M_1(t)M_1(t+\tau)M_2(t)M_2(t+\tau)}{\{[M_1^2(t)R_{01} + M_2^2(t)R_{02}][M_1^2(t+\tau)R_{01} + M_2^2(t+\tau)R_{02}]\}^{1-\nu/2}}$$

and by definition

$$\psi_3(\tau) = \langle \psi_3(\tau, t) \rangle = \frac{\omega}{2\pi} \int_0^{2\pi/\omega} \psi_3(\tau, t)\, dt. \tag{5-56}$$

Let $\omega_1 = \omega_2 = \omega_m$ and then expand $\psi_3(\tau)$ into its Fourier series representation which will be possible because M_1 and M_2 will now be similar periodic functions having the same period. Of course, a similar procedure can be used if one is not able to make this assumption and $\omega_1 \neq \omega_2$. With our assumption, we can write

$$\psi_3(\tau) = a_0 + \sum_{n=1}^{\infty} (a_n \cos n\omega_m\tau + b_n \sin n\omega_m\tau). \tag{5-57}$$

The constant term in the series is evaluated in the following manner.

$$\begin{aligned} a_0 &= \frac{2Q_1(\nu)R_{\tau 1}R_{\tau 2}}{4\pi^2} \int_0^{2\pi/\omega} \int_0^{2\pi/\omega} \psi_3(t, \tau)\, dt\, d\tau, \\ &= \frac{2Q_1(\nu)R_{\tau 1}R_{\tau 2}}{4\pi^2 R_0^{2(1-\nu/2)}} \left[\int_0^{2\pi} \frac{(1 + m \cos u)\, du}{(1 + \lambda \cos u)^{1-\nu/2}} \right]^2 \end{aligned} \tag{5-58}$$

where

$$\begin{aligned} m &= m_1 - m_2 \\ R_0 &= R_{01} + R_{02} \\ \lambda &= \frac{2}{R_0}(m_1 R_{01} - m_2 R_{02}). \end{aligned} \tag{5-59}$$

Because of the assumption of small modulation indices, λ is small compared to unity. Therefore the denominator in the integral of Eq. (5-58) can be expanded into a binomial series and approximated by retaining only the first two terms. The result is

$$a_0 = \frac{2Q_1(\nu)R_{\tau 1}R_{\tau 2}}{R^{2(1-\nu/2)}} \left[1 + \frac{m}{2}\lambda\left(\frac{\nu}{2} - 1\right) \right]^2. \tag{5-60}$$

Similarly we compute

$$a_n = \frac{2Q_1(\nu)R_{\tau 1}R_{\tau 2}}{\pi^2} \int_0^{2\pi/\omega} \int_0^{2\pi/\omega} \psi_3(t, \tau) \cos n\omega_m \tau \, dt \, d\tau, \tag{5-61}$$

$$= \frac{2Q_1(\nu)R_{\tau 1}R_{\tau 2}}{\pi^2 R_0^{2(1-\nu/2)}} \left[\int_0^{2\pi} \frac{(1 + m \cos u) \cos nu}{(1 + \lambda \cos u)^{1-\nu/2}} \, du \right]^2 .$$

The denominator is once again expanded and approximated by retaining only the first two terms. It is found that if only the terms involving the first power of the modulation indices are kept, all coefficients can be deleted except a_1, and

$$a_1 = \frac{2Q_1(\nu)R_{\tau 1}R_{\tau 2}}{R_0^{2(1-\nu/2)}} \left[m + \lambda \left(\frac{\nu}{2} - 1 \right) \right]^2 . \tag{5-62}$$

An analogous development shows that all the b_n coefficients vanish.

Collecting results, we have

$$\psi_3(\tau) \approx \frac{2Q_1(\nu)R_{\tau 1}R_{\tau 2}}{R_0^{2(1-\nu/2)}} \left[1 + \frac{m}{2} \lambda \left(\frac{\nu}{2} - 1 \right) \right]^2 \left(1 + \left\{ \frac{m + \lambda \left[\left(\frac{\nu}{2} \right) - 1 \right]}{1 + \frac{m}{2} \lambda \left(\frac{\nu}{2} - 1 \right)} \right\}^2 \right) \cos \omega_m \tau . \tag{5-63}$$

The effective modulation index of the spectral band surrounding the difference frequency, when only the first powers of the modulation indices are retained can be shown to be, [49]

$$m_e \approx \frac{\sqrt{2}}{1 + \dfrac{R_{02}}{R_{01}}} \left\{ m_1 \left[\nu - 1 + \frac{R_{02}}{R_{01}} \right] - m_2 \left[\frac{R_{02}}{R_{01}} (\nu - 1) + 1 \right] \right\} . \tag{5-64}$$

6 SERIES APPROXIMATIONS

6.1 GENERAL ANALYTICAL TECHNIQUES

Chapters 6 and 7 discuss various attempts that have been made to discover general methods for handling the result of nonlinear transformations of random processes. In a certain sense these methods have been successful because in each case, when Gaussian processes are assumed for input signals, the results agree with other more specialized techniques such as those presented in the preceding chapters. The general methods are universal from the point-of-view that the theories do not limit themselves to Gaussian processes or to rather restrictive types of transformations. However, one should not become too enthusiastic about generalized analytical techniques for treating nonlinear devices. Generalization only comes at a price. In Chapter 6 the penalty for generalized methods lies in long and somewhat tedious computations. In Chapter 7 it will be shown that the penalty lies in the requirement for obtaining solutions of rather involved and difficult boundary value problems. Nevertheless, one can hardly argue against the utility of general analytical techniques, no matter what the penalty, when confronted with a practical problem for which an *elegant* solution cannot be found and for which the *ordinary* methods are not applicable.

Whenever one is confronted with a difficult nonlinear transformation which does not lend itself to simple techniques, the obvious course of action is to resort to some sort of approximation. Several alternatives are possible. The frequency function of the random process may be approximated by a series representation, the nonlinear transformation may be approximated, or an appropriate series representation might be used for the combination of nonlinearity and random process statistics. All these alternatives will be illustrated.

A naïve, but direct approach would be to approximate everything by power series. This procedure would probably work, at least in theory, for almost any problem, but the labor involved might truly be prodigious. The logical and conservative approach is to try to utilize only a few terms of series expansions. A little experience quickly indicates that an important phase of series solution techniques lies in the choice of an expansion function which closely represents the desired nonlinearity characteristics with the minimum number of terms.

6.2 FIRST PROBABILITY FREQUENCY FUNCTIONS

A novice's rule of thumb in chess is: *when in doubt, push a pawn.* By the same token, a rule of thumb for dealing with nonlinear transformations of random processes might well be: *when in doubt, compute the output moments.* This rule is the result of the observation in Chapter 3 that the output moments are usually quite readily computed. Thus, if the transformation of $x(t)$ is defined by

$$y(t) = h[x(t)], \tag{6-1}$$

then the first order moments of the output signal are

$$E\{y_n(t)\} = \int h^n[x(t)]f[x(t)]\,dx, \tag{6-2}$$

where $f(x)$ is the frequency function of the input process, $x(t)$.

It is well-known that many frequency functions can be approximated by a series of polynomials whose coefficients are determined by the moments of the output distribution computed from Eq. (6-2). In particular it has been shown that the output distribution often can be readily approximated by a few terms if a fortuitous choice is made for the expansion polynomials. Several special cases have been selected for illustrative examples.

6.2.1 *GRAM-CHARLIER SERIES*

Define the function $\phi(u)$ as

$$\phi(u) = \frac{1}{\sqrt{2\pi}}\,e^{-u^2/2}. \tag{6-3}$$

This function is related to the Hermite polynomials $H_i(u)$, by the expression

$$\phi^{(j)}(u) = \frac{d^j}{du^j}\left[\frac{1}{\sqrt{2\pi}}\,e^{-u^2/2}H_j(u)\right]. \tag{6-4}$$

The ϕ functions and the Hermite polynomials are biorthogonal because they satisfy the relation

(6-5) $$\int_{-\infty}^{\infty} H_j(u)\phi^{(i)}(u)\,du = \delta_{ij},$$

where δ_{ij} is the Kronecker-delta function. We can expand almost any *reasonable* frequency function in a series of the form, [51]

(6-6) $$f(u) = \sum_{j=0}^{\infty} a_j\phi^{(j)}(u).$$

The coefficients are determined by applying Eq. (6-5) to Eq. (6-6). The result is

(6-7) $$a_j = \frac{(-1)^j}{j!}\int_{-\infty}^{\infty} H_j(u)f(u)\,du.$$

Usually the substitution $v = u - \overline{u}/\sigma$ is made before making the expansion. This is done so that the second and third terms of series will vanish. We will use the notation:

(6-8) $$\overline{u} = \nu_1 = \text{the first moment of } u$$

$$\nu_n = n'\text{th moment of } u$$

$$\sigma^2 = \nu_2 - \nu_1^2 = \text{the variance of } u.$$

Equation (6-6) is replaced by

(6-9) $$f(u) = g(v) = \sum_{j=0}^{\infty} c_j\phi^{(j)}(v),$$

and Eq. (6-7) by

(6-10) $$c_j = \frac{(-1)^j}{j!}\int_{-\infty}^{\infty} H_j\left(\frac{u - \overline{u}}{\sigma}\right) f(u)\,\frac{du}{\sigma}.$$

From Eq. (6-10), one sees that $c_0 = \frac{1}{\sigma}$, $c_1 = c_2 = 0$. The central moments are defined by the relation

(6-11) $$\mu_i = \int_{-\infty}^{\infty} (u - \overline{u})f(u)\,du,$$

and the standard moments about the mean as

(6-12) $$\alpha_i = \frac{\mu_i}{\sigma_i}.$$

A few of the coefficients c_j are:

(6-13) $$c_0 = \frac{1}{\sigma}$$

$$c_1 = c_2 = 0$$

$$c_3 = -\frac{1}{3!}\,\alpha_3$$

$$c_4 = \frac{1}{4!}(\alpha_4 - 3)$$

$$c_5 = -\frac{1}{5!}(\alpha_5 - 10\alpha_3)$$

$$c_6 = \frac{1}{6!}(\alpha_6 - 15\alpha_4 + 30).$$

Expressions for μ_i in terms of ν_i can be found from the integral relation

$$\mu_i = \int_{-\infty}^{\infty} (u - \overline{u})f(u)\, du. \tag{6-14}$$

Using Eq. (6-14) and previous definitions, one can obtain the following:

$$\begin{aligned} \mu_2 &= \nu_2 - \nu_1^2 \\ \mu_3 &= \nu_3 - 3\nu_2\nu_1 + 2\nu_1^3 \\ \mu_4 &= \nu_4 - 4\nu_3\nu_1 + 6\nu_2\nu_1^2 - 3\nu_1^4 \\ \mu_5 &= \nu_5 - 5\nu_4\nu_1 + 10\nu_3\nu_1^2 - 10\nu_2\nu_1^3 + 4\nu_1^5 \\ \mu_6 &= \nu_6 - 6\nu_5\nu_1 + 15\nu_4\nu_1^2. \end{aligned} \tag{6-15}$$

The process of applying the Gram-Charlier expansion can be summarized in five steps.

(i) Compute the moments of the output distribution.
(ii) Find the central moments from Eq. (6-15).
(iii) Obtain the corresponding standard central moments from Eq. (6-12).
(iv) Compute the series coefficients using Eq. (6-13).
(v) Write the series representation of $f(u)$ using Eq. (6-9).

Careful investigation of the convergence of the Gram-Charlier series has shown that if only a few terms are computed, the *best* grouping of terms in Eq. (6-9) is not that associated with taking terms in their *natural order*. Various regrouped series have been proposed, but the Edgeworth series are generally employed in most applications. The grouping proposed by Edgeworth is

$$\begin{aligned} &0 \\ &0, 3 \\ &0, 3, 4, 6 \\ &0, 3, 4, 6, 5, 7, 9. \end{aligned} \tag{6-16}$$

This list implies that if the 0 and 3 terms are used as the first approximation, the addition of terms 4 and 6 gives the next order approximation, and so forth.

6.2.2 LAGUERRE SERIES

If the true output probability distribution vanishes for negative values of the random process, an expansion of the frequency function in terms of the Gram-Charlier expansions will not converge very rapidly. A more suitable expansion is

$$f(u) = \sum_{j=0}^{\infty} a_j e^{-u} u^{\alpha} L_j^{\alpha}(u), \tag{6-17}$$

where $L_j^{\alpha}(u)$ is the generalized Laguerre polynomial which can be defined by a Rodrigue's formula:

$$L_j^{\alpha}(u) = \frac{e^{u} u^{-\alpha}}{j!} \frac{d^j}{du^j} (e^{-u} u^{j+\alpha}). \tag{6-18}$$

The orthogonality relation for this polynomial is

$$\int_0^{\infty} e^{-u} u^{\alpha} L_j^{\alpha}(u) L_i^{\alpha}(u)\, du = \frac{\Gamma(\alpha + j + 1)\, \delta_{ij}}{j!}. \tag{6-19}$$

By combining Eq. (6-19) and Eq. (6-17), the expansion coefficients are found to be

$$a_j = \frac{j!}{\Gamma(\alpha + j + 1)} \int_0^{\infty} L_j^{\alpha}(u) f(u)\, du. \tag{6-20}$$

Make the change of variable $v = u/\beta$ and Eq. (6-17) becomes

$$f(u) = g(v) = \sum_{j=0}^{\infty} C_i e^{-v} v^{\alpha} L_j^{\alpha}(v), \tag{6-21}$$

where

$$\begin{aligned} C_j &= \frac{j!}{\Gamma(\alpha + j + 1)} \int_0^{\infty} L_j^{\alpha}(v) g(v)\, dv \\ &= \frac{j!}{\Gamma(\alpha + j + 1)} \int_0^{\infty} L_j^{\alpha}\left(\frac{u}{\beta}\right) f(u) \frac{du}{\beta}. \end{aligned} \tag{6-22}$$

Some of the first few Laguerre polynomials are

$$\begin{aligned} L_0^{\alpha}(u) &= 1 \\ L_1^{\alpha}(u) &= 1 + \alpha - u \\ 2L_2^{\alpha}(u) &= (\alpha + 1)(\alpha + 2) - 2u(\alpha + 2) + u^2 \\ 6L_3^{\alpha}(u) &= (\alpha + 1)(\alpha + 2)(\alpha + 3) \\ &\quad - 3u(\alpha + 2)(\alpha + 3) + 3u^2(\alpha + 3) - u^3. \end{aligned} \tag{6-23}$$

Substitute Eq. (6-23) in (6-22) to evaluate the first two coefficients.

$$C_1 = \frac{1}{\beta\Gamma(\alpha + 2)} \left(1 + \alpha - \frac{\nu_1}{\beta}\right). \tag{6-24}$$

$$C_2 = \frac{1}{\beta\Gamma(\alpha + 3)} \left[(\alpha + 1)(\alpha + 2) - \frac{2\nu_1}{\beta}(\alpha + 2) + \frac{\nu_2}{\beta^2} \right]. \tag{6-25}$$

Since α and β are arbitrary constants in Eq. (6-21) and Eq. (6-22), one can choose these constants so that $C_1 = C_2 = 0$. This choice is made by equating Eq. (6-24) and Eq. (6-25) to zero and solving the resulting two simultaneous equations. The solutions are

$$\alpha = \frac{\nu_1^2}{\nu_2 - \nu_1^2} - 1 = \frac{\nu_1^2}{\sigma^2} - 1, \tag{6-26}$$

$$\beta = \frac{\nu_2 - \nu_1^2}{\nu_1} = \frac{\sigma^2}{\nu_1}. \tag{6-27}$$

Using this choice of constants, the first four expansion coefficients become

$$C_0 = \frac{1}{\beta\Gamma(\alpha + 1)} = \frac{\nu_1}{\sigma^2\Gamma\left(\frac{\nu_1^2}{\sigma^2}\right)} \tag{6-28}$$

$$C_1 = C_2 = 0$$

$$C_3 = \frac{1}{\beta\Gamma(\alpha + 4)} \left[\frac{\nu_2}{\beta^2}(\alpha + 3) - \frac{\nu_3}{\beta^3} \right].$$

The coefficients, other than C_0 and C_3, are so complicated that, in practice, expansions in Laguerre series are not usually made unless the first term is in itself a sufficiently good approximation. Retaining only the first term, the approximate frequency function is

$$f(u) = \frac{\nu_1}{\sigma^2\Gamma\left(\frac{\nu_1^2}{\sigma^2}\right)} \left(\frac{\nu_1 u}{\sigma^2}\right)^{(\nu_1^2/\sigma^2) - 1} \cdot \exp\left(-\nu_1 u/\sigma^2\right). \tag{6-29}$$

6.2.3 Q-POLYNOMIALS

Anyone who has tried to use series expansions for frequency functions has very likely encountered the frustration of having to calculate more than the few terms used in text books for illustrative examples. Yet there doesn't seem to be any simple rule for deciding which type of orthogonal polynomials will give the best approximation with the fewest number of terms and the least calculation effort. Young,[52] has developed a technique which points the way for a good approximation when the input process is Gaussian and a particular class of nonlinearity is involved. He noted that since non-Gaussian processes in physical systems are generally a consequence of nonlinear transformations by devices having characteristics easily approximated by a few terms of a power series, it would be convenient to make the frequency function expansion in terms of polynomials which are related to powers of the Gaussian frequency function. Young called these the *Q polynomials*.

The first order Q polynomials are nothing more than normalized Hermite polynomials. The first polynomial is

$$Q_n^{(1)}(u) = \frac{(-1)^n}{\sqrt{n!}} e^{-u^2/2} \frac{d^n}{du^n} e^{-u^2/2}, \tag{6-30}$$

with the orthogonality relation

$$\frac{1}{\sqrt{2\pi}} \int_{-\infty}^{\infty} Q_n^{(1)}(u) Q_m^{(1)}(u) e^{-u^2/2}\, du = \delta_{mn}. \tag{6-31}$$

Now define a new variable,

$$v = u^k; \qquad k \text{ is an integer.} \tag{6-32}$$

Insert this change of variable into the orthogonality condition. Then for k an odd integer

$$\frac{1}{k} \frac{1}{\sqrt{2\pi}} \int_{-\infty}^{\infty} Q_n^{(k)}(v) Q_m^{(k)}(v) \frac{e^{-\frac{v^{2/k}}{2}}}{v^{1-1/k}}\, dv = \delta_{mn}, \tag{6-33}$$

and for k an even integer

$$\frac{2}{k} \frac{1}{\sqrt{2\pi}} \int_{0}^{\infty} Q_n^{(k)}(v) Q_m^{(k)}(v) \frac{e^{-\frac{v^{2/k}}{2}}}{v^{1-1/k}}\, dv = \delta_{mn}. \tag{6-34}$$

The frequency function after the nonlinear transformation can be represented by the series

$$f(z) = \sum_{n=0}^{\infty} c_n Q_n^{(k)}(z) \frac{e^{-\frac{z^{2/k}}{2}}}{z^{1-1/k}}, \tag{6-35}$$

where for k odd

$$C_n = \frac{1}{k} \frac{1}{\sqrt{2\pi}} \int_{-\infty}^{\infty} Q_n^{(k)}(z) f(z)\, dz, \tag{6-36}$$

and for k even

$$C_n = \frac{2}{k} \frac{1}{\sqrt{2\pi}} \int_{\infty}^{\infty} Q_n^{(k)}(z) f(z)\, dz. \tag{6-37}$$

The various polynomials of first order can be generated from Eqs. (6-36) and (6-37) by defining $Q_0^{(1)} = 1$ and then applying the Schmidt Orthogonality process. For example, some of the first polynomials are found to be

$$Q_0^{(1)} = 1 \qquad Q_2^{(2)} = \frac{z^2 - 1}{\sqrt{2}} \tag{6-38}$$

$$Q_1^{(1)} = z \qquad Q_3^{(1)} = \frac{z^3 - 3z}{\sqrt{6}}.$$

The coefficients C_n corresponding to the first order Q polynomials in Eq. (6-38) are

$$C_0 = \frac{1}{\sqrt{2\pi}} \tag{6-39}$$

$$C_1 = \frac{E\{z\}}{\sqrt{2\pi}}$$

$$C_2 = \frac{E\{z^2\} - 1}{\sqrt{4\pi}}$$

$$C_3 = \frac{E\{z^3\} - 3E\{z\}}{\sqrt{12\pi}}.$$

A few of the second order Q polynomials are

$$Q_0^{(2)}(z) = 1 \qquad Q_2^{(2)}(z) = \frac{z^2 - 6z + 3}{\sqrt{4!}} \tag{6-40}$$

$$Q_1^{(2)}(z) = \frac{z - 1}{\sqrt{2!}} \qquad Q_3^{(2)}(z) = \frac{z^3 - 15z^2 + 45z - 15}{\sqrt{6!}}.$$

6.3 CORRELATION FUNCTION EXPANSIONS

Although the expansion techniques described in Sec. 6.2 are fairly familiar, it is not as well known that these same methods are useful in nonlinear problems when applied to obtaining series representations for correlation functions. The general applicability of series representations for correlation functions is described in Sec. 6.4. In this section we will present two interesting examples which serve as a motivation for the later theoretical development. The first illustration describes a scheme for using linear filters to evaluate the coefficients for a series representation of a correlation function. This method is merely an application of the property of matched filters. The second example treats a random impulse process in which the nature of the impulse waveshape can be inferred from knowledge of the output signal's correlation function.

6.3.1 DETERMINATION OF CORRELATION FUNCTION COEFFICIENTS

Lampard has shown that by using appropriate filters, an electrical circuit can be constructed which approximates a signal's correlation function by determining the coefficients for the function's series representation, [53]. We start by assuming that the correlation function $\psi(\tau)$ is sufficiently well-behaved so that it can be represented by a series of orthogonal weighting functions. Write the representation in the form

(6-41) $$\psi(\tau) = \sum_{n=0}^{\infty} a_n \theta_n(\tau)[p(\tau)]^{\gamma}; \qquad 0 \leq \tau < \infty,$$

where the $\{\theta_n(\tau)\}$ are a set of orthonormal polynomials with respect to the weight function $p(\tau)$ and defined for all real positive values of τ. Thus

(6-42) $$\int_0^{\infty} \theta_n(\tau)\theta_m(\tau)p(\tau)\, d\tau = \delta_{mn}.$$

The coefficients a_n are obtained in the usual manner by combining Eqs. (6-41) and (6-42). We find

(6-43) $$a_n = \int_0^{\infty} \psi(\tau)\theta_n(\tau)p^{1-\gamma}(\tau)\, d\tau.$$

Lampard next introduces the concept of an orthogonal linear filter. We will examine this concept and show how it can be related to the series representation of $\psi(\tau)$. Consider the system shown in Figure 6-1.

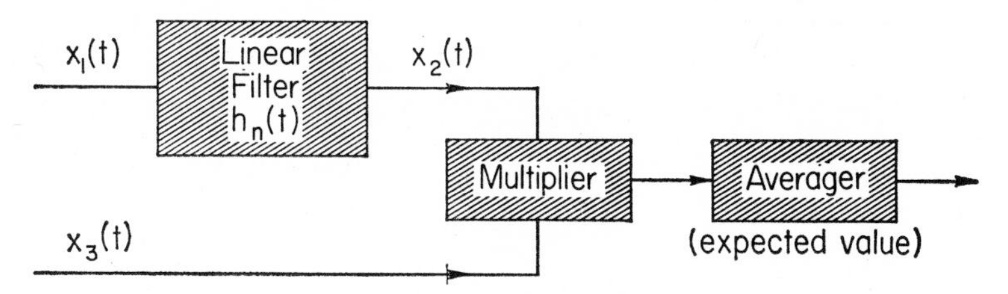

Figure 6-1. Orthogonal Filter

If the impulse response of the filter is $h_n(t)$, the output signal can be written as

(6-44) $$X_2(t) = \int_0^{\infty} X_1(t-u)h_n(u)\, du.$$

Hence the output signal from the multiplier is

(6-45) $$X_2(t)X_3(t) = \int_0^{\infty} X_1(t-u)X_3(t)h_n(u)\, du.$$

Assuming that all the functions are sufficiently well-behaved to permit changes in the order of integration, the expected value of the multiplied signals is

(6-46) $$E\{X_2(t)X_3(t)\} = \int_0^{\infty} E\{X_1(t-u)X_3(t)\}h_n(u)\, du$$
$$= \int_0^{\infty} \psi_{13}(u)h_n(u)\, du.$$

Compare Eqs. (6-46) and (6-43). Evidently the coefficient a_n is equal to $E\{X_2(t)X_3(t)\}$ provided that the choice of the linear filter's impulse response function is

(6-47) $$h_n(t) = \theta_n(t)p^{1-\gamma}(t).$$

An *orthogonal filter* is defined as a linear filter whose impulse response function satisfies Eq. (6-47). Obviously if we had a set of linear filters for the system shown in Figure 6-1, we could use them sequentially, or in parallel, to measure each coefficient a_n required to determine the series representation of the correlation function.

It is perhaps at least of practical interest to demonstrate that it is possible to obtain a physical realization of orthogonal filters. Consider the particular weight function

$$p(t) = \alpha e^{-\alpha t}. \tag{6-48}$$

Notice that the polynomials $\theta_n(t)$ and hence the impulse responses of the orthogonal filters, $h_n(t)$, depend only on the weight function $p(t)$ and the parameter γ. Two particular examples of weighting functions will be discussed.

example (*i*): Let

$$\begin{aligned} p(t) &= \alpha e^{-\alpha t} \\ \gamma &= 0. \end{aligned} \tag{6-49}$$

The polynomials corresponding to this weight function are the Laguerre polynomials which can be represented by the series

$$L_n(\alpha t) = \sum_{q=0}^{n} \frac{n!}{(n-q)!} \frac{(-\alpha t)^q}{q!q!}. \tag{6-50}$$

The appropriate orthogonality relation corresponding to Eq. (6-42) for the Laguerre polynomials is

$$\int_0^{\alpha} L_n(\alpha t) L_m(\alpha t) \alpha e^{-\alpha t}\, dt = \delta_{mn}. \tag{6-51}$$

We shall need the Laplace transforms of the following functions:

$$\mathcal{L}\{\alpha e^{-\alpha t} L_n(\alpha t)\} = \frac{\alpha}{s+\alpha}\left(\frac{s}{s+\alpha}\right)^n, \tag{6-52}$$

$$\mathcal{L}\left\{\frac{\alpha}{2} e^{-\alpha t/2} L_n(\alpha t)\right\} = \frac{\alpha/2}{s+\alpha/2}\left(\frac{s-\alpha/2}{s+\alpha/2}\right)^n, \tag{6-53}$$

where s is the transform variable corresponding to t.

Consider the electrical circuit configuration shown in Figure 6-2. In this circuit isolating devices are inserted between sections of the network.

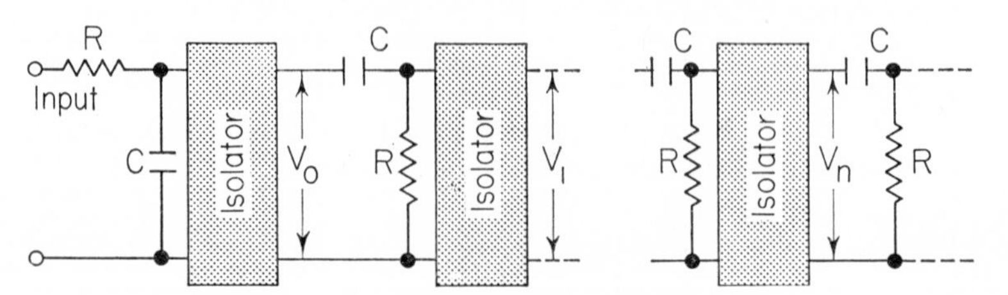

Figure 6-2. Laguerre Function Filter, $\gamma = 0$

After applying standard circuit analysis techniques, it can be shown that

$$\mathfrak{L}\{V_{n+1}(t)\} = \frac{s}{s+\alpha}\,\mathfrak{L}\{V_n(t)\}, \tag{6-54}$$

where $\alpha = \dfrac{1}{RC}$ and $0 \leq n < N$. Therefore, it follows that the impulse response $h_n(t)$, which is equal to the signal $V_n(t)$ generated when a impulse signal is applied to the input of the network, satisfies the Laplace transform relation

$$\mathfrak{L}\{h_n(t)\} = \frac{\alpha}{s+\alpha}\left(\frac{s}{s+\alpha}\right)^n. \tag{6-55}$$

Compare Eqs. (6-55) and (6-52). Because of the uniqueness property of Laplace transforms, it follows that the impulse response of the orthogonal filters is

$$h_n(t) = \alpha e^{-\alpha t} L_n(\alpha t), \tag{6-56}$$

and these can be realized by the circuit shown in Figure 6-2. Note that Eq. (6-56) corresponds to Eq. (6-47) with $\gamma = 0$.

example (ii): Let

$$\begin{aligned} p(t) &= \alpha e^{-\alpha t}, \\ \gamma &= 1/2. \end{aligned} \tag{6-57}$$

Refer to the lattice structure shown in Figure 6-3.

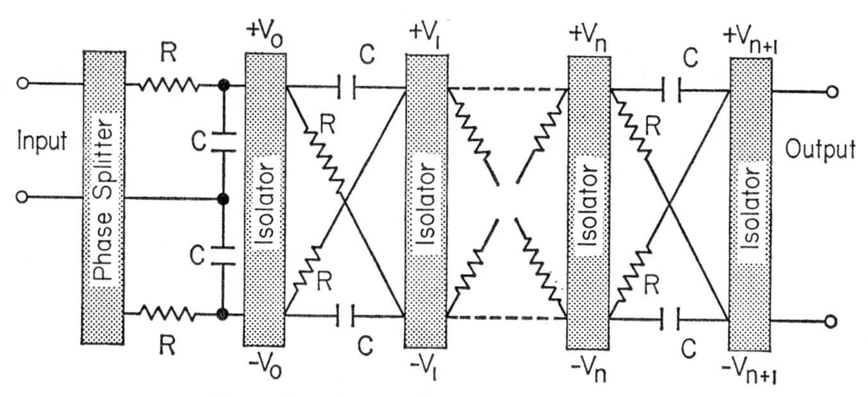

Figure 6-3. Laguerre Function Filter, $\gamma = \frac{1}{2}$

Analogous to Eq. (6-54), the recurrence relation applicable to this network can be shown to be

$$\mathfrak{L}\{V_{n+1}(t)\} = \left[\frac{s-\alpha/2}{s+\alpha/2}\right]\mathfrak{L}\{V_n(t)\}, \tag{6-58}$$

where, in this case, $\alpha = \dfrac{2}{RC}$.

The impulse response function must now satisfy the relation

$$\mathfrak{L}\{h_n(t)\} = \frac{\alpha/2}{s + \alpha/2}\left[\frac{s - \alpha/2}{s + \alpha/2}\right]^n. \tag{6-59}$$

Compare Eqs. (6-59) and (6-52). From this comparison it follows that

$$h_n(t) = \alpha/2\, L_n(\alpha t)e^{-\alpha t/2}, \tag{6-60}$$

which, except for a constant factor, has the same form as Eq. (6-47) with $\gamma = 1/2$.

6.3.2 *ESTIMATION OF NOISE PULSE SHAPES*

After a signal has been processed by a nonlinear device, very little information concerning the original time series can be inferred from knowledge of the output correlation function. However, Horton, [54, 55], has shown that even after a nonlinear transformation such as that of finding a process's correlation function, it is possible to infer properties of the original time function. We shall confine our attention to a process which consists of a sequence of pulses with shape $F(t)$. These pulses arrive at randomly spaced intervals. From a knowledge of the correlation function of the process we shall try to infer the original pulse shape $F(t)$. Obviously it is too much to hope that one can reconstruct the waveshape from the correlation function for any situation. But if $F(t)$ can be represented by a series related to the ordinary Gram-Charlier series, Horton demonstrated a method for reconstructing $F(t)$ from its correlation function.

Suppose that, as in many seismographic situations $F(t)$ can be represented by the series

$$F(t) = \sum_{m=0}^{\infty} b_m \Phi^{(m)}(t/T), \tag{6-61}$$

where

$$\Phi^{(0)}(x) = \frac{1}{\sqrt{2\pi}} \exp(-x^2/2) \tag{6-62}$$

and

$$\Phi^{(n)}(x) = \frac{d}{dx}\Phi^{(n-1)}(x). \tag{6-63}$$

Pulses of this general type also occur in electroencephalographic studies.

The input process can be written as

$$y(t) = \sum_{k=-\infty}^{+\infty} F(t - t_k). \tag{6-64}$$

For this type of random process, Rice [9], has shown that the correlation function of $y(t)$ is

$$\psi(\tau) = N\int_{-\infty}^{\infty} F(t)F(t+\tau)\,dt + [E\{y(t)\}]^2, \tag{6-65}$$

where N is the average number of pulses $F(t)$ that occur per second and

(6-66) $$E\{y(t)\} = N \int_{-\infty}^{\infty} F(t)\,dt.$$

Substitute Eq. (6-61) in Eq. (6-65) and make the change of variables

(6-67) $$x = t/T \qquad y = \tau/t.$$

One finds

(6-68) $$\psi(\tau) = NT \int_{-\infty}^{\infty} \left[\sum_{m=1}^{\infty} b_m \Phi^{(m)}(x) \right] \left[\sum_{m=1}^{\infty} b_m \Phi^{(m)}(x+y) \right] dx,$$

where for the moment we neglect $[E\{y(t)\}]^2$.

Consider the integral

(6-69) $$I = \int_{-\infty}^{\infty} \Phi^{(m)}(x)\Phi^{(m)}(x+y)\,dx.$$

After integrating by parts

(6-70) $$I = -\int_{-\infty}^{\infty} \Phi^{(m+1)}(x)\Phi^{(m-1)}(x+y)\,dx.$$

Iterate this integration n-times and we find

(6-71) $$I_{mn} = (-1)^n \int_{-\infty}^{\infty} \Phi^{(m+n)}(x)\Phi^{(0)}(x+y)\,dx.$$

But note that

(6-72) $$\Phi^{(m+n)}(x)\Phi^{(0)}(x+y) = (-1)^{m+n} \frac{1}{2\pi} H_{m+n}(x) \exp\{-[x^2 + (x+y)^2]^{1/2}\}.$$

Substitute Eq. (6-72) in Eq. (6-71), and with a little rearranging of terms;

(6-73) $$I_{mn} = \frac{(-1)^m}{2\pi\sqrt{2}} e^{-y^2/4} \int_{-\infty}^{\infty} H_{m+n}\left(\frac{u}{\sqrt{2}} - \frac{y}{2}\right) \exp(-u^2/2)\,du.$$

Apply the addition formula for Hermite polynomials [17],

(6-74) $$H_p(s+t) = 2^{-p/2} \sum_{q=0}^{p} \binom{p}{q} H_{p-q}(s\sqrt{2})H_q(t\sqrt{2}),$$

to Eq. (6-73). Because all the integrals will vanish except the one corresponding to $q = 0$, the manipulation yields

(6-75) $$I_{mn} = (-1)^m 2^{-(m+n+1)/2} \Phi^{(m+n)}(y/\sqrt{2}).$$

Combine Eqs. (6-75) and (6-68) to obtain the desired expansion of the correlation function

(6-76) $$\psi(\tau) = \sum_{m,n=0}^{\infty} (-1)_m a_m a_n \Phi^{(m+n)} \left(\frac{\tau}{T\sqrt{2}}\right) + \sqrt{2}NTa_0^2,$$

where

$$a_m = \left(\frac{NT}{2^m\sqrt{2}}\right)^{1/2} b_m. \tag{6-77}$$

Notice that the terms corresponding to odd values of $m + n$ vanish. This is expected because of the symmetry of the correlation function. Equation (6-76) can be arranged as follows to correspond to the usual Gram-Charlier configuration:

$$\psi(\tau) = \sum_{p=0}^{\infty} c_{2p}\Phi^{(2p)}\left(\frac{\tau}{T\sqrt{2}}\right) + \sqrt{2}NTc_0, \tag{6-78}$$

where

$$c_{2p} = \sum_{m,n=0}^{2p} (m + n = 2p)(-1)^m a_m a_n. \tag{6-79}$$

As the situation stands at this point, we see that knowledge of the correlation function $\psi(\tau)$ permits us to calculate the coefficients c_{2p}. But notice that in Eq. (6-79), the relations for the coefficients are nonlinear in the a_i so that a sequence of values $\{c_p\}$ will not yield a unique sequence $\{a_i\}$. Horton noted that if one retains only the first four terms of the expansion in Eq. (6-78), then he can in turn compute the first four coefficients for the expansion of the pulse shape in Eq. (6-61). If only the first four terms are retained, it can be shown that the first four even coefficients are

$$\begin{aligned} c_0 &= a_0^2 \\ c_2 &= 2a_0a_2 - a_1^2 \\ c_4 &= -2a_1a_3 + a_2^2 \\ c_6 &= -a_3^2. \end{aligned} \tag{6-80}$$

There are eight sets of real constants $\{a_i\}$ which satisfy Eq. (6-80). Four of these sets are simply the negative of the other four and so may be rejected. Of the remaining four, two are equivalent to replacing the time t by $-t$ in the other two sets and so may also be neglected. Falling back on experimental evidence, [55], it was found that the two remaining coefficient sets give rise to very similar approximations to $F(t)$. At this last step, one would have to have some *a priori* information before a choice between the final two coefficient sets could be made. Although this does not lead to a *clear* solution, it is rather remarkable that any information concerning the original pulse shapes could be gleaned from the correlation function of the process.

6.4 SECOND-ORDER FREQUENCY FUNCTION

Obviously if first-order frequency functions can be expanded into useful series representations, one would expect that similar useful generalized expansions would also exist for higher order frequency functions. Of course such expansions do exist and have often appeared in the statistical journals. A particularly useful expansion for our purposes was introduced by Barrett and Lampard, [56]. The following development closely follows their original work.

Let $f(x_1, x_2)$ be a second-order frequency function for the variables x_1 and x_2. The corresponding first-order frequency functions are then

(6-81)
$$f_1(x_1) = \int f(x_1, x_2)\, dx_2$$
$$f_2(x_2) = \int f(x_1, x_2)\, dx_1.$$

Using the first-order frequency functions as weighting functions, we can construct two sets of orthonormal polynomials $\{\theta_{1n}(x_1)\}$ and $\{\theta_{2n}(x_2)\}$ from the integral relation

(6-82)
$$\int f_1(x_1)\theta_{1m}(x_1)\theta_{1n}(x_1)\, dx_1 = \delta_{mn}$$
$$\int f_2(x_2)\theta_{2m}(x_2)\theta_{2n}(x_2)\, dx_2 = \delta_{mn}.$$

If we assume that it is permissible to expand $f(x_1, x_2)$ in terms of these two sets of orthonormal functions, then

(6-83)
$$f(x_1, x_2) = f_1(x_1)f_2(x_2) \sum_{m,n=0}^{\infty} a_{mn}\theta_{1m}(x_1)\theta_{2n}(x_2).$$

By employing Eq. (6-82) in Eq. (6-83), we can evaluate the expansion coefficients,

(6-84)
$$a_{mn} = \iint f(x_1, x_2)\theta_{1m}(x_1)\theta_{2n}(x_2)\, dx_1\, dx_2.$$

Barrett and Lampard restricted themselves to a class F of frequency functions $f(x_1, x_2)$ for which the matrix (a_{mn}) is diagonal. In accordance with their notation, we will add the letter F after all equations which are only valid for distributions which are members of the class F.

Therefore, for all $f(x_1, x_2)$ belonging to class F,

(6-85)F
$$f(x_1, x_2) = f_1(x_1)f_2(x_2) \sum_{n=0}^{\infty} a_n\theta_{1n}(x_1)\theta_{2n}(x_2),$$

where now the expansion coefficients are

(6-86)F
$$a_n = \iint f(x_1, x_2)\theta_{1n}(x_1)\theta_{2n}(x_2)\, dx_1\, dx_2.$$

The next step is to determine the form of the orthonormal polynomials of degree 0 and 1. As usual, define $\theta_{10}(x_1) = \theta_{20}(x_2) = 1$. Then from Eq. (6-82)

(6-87)
$$\int f_1(x_1)\cdot 1\cdot 1\, dx_1 = 1.$$

This result is expected because $f_1(x_1)$ is a probability frequency function. Continuing with the Gram-Schmidt procedure for generating orthonormal functions, from Eq. (6-82) we obtain

(6-88) $$\int f_1(x_1)\cdot(x_1 - \mu_1)\cdot 1\cdot dx_1 = 0$$

(6-89) $$\int f_1(x_1)\cdot(x_1 - \mu_1)(x_1 - \mu_1)\, dx_1 = \sigma_1^2,$$

with analogous results for $f_2(x_2)$. The symbols μ_1 and σ_1 denote the mean value and standard deviation. It can be seen that

(6-90) $$\theta_{10}(x_1) = 1 \qquad \theta_{20}(x_2) = 1$$

$$\theta_{11}(x_1) = \frac{x_1 - \mu_1}{\sigma_1} \qquad \theta_{21}(x_2) = \frac{x_2 - \mu_2}{\sigma_2}.$$

Combine Eqs. (6-90) and (6-86) to obtain

(6-91) $$a_0 = 1$$

$$a_1 = \frac{1}{\sigma_1\sigma_2} E\{(x_1 - \mu_1)(x_1 - \mu_2)\} = \rho.$$

a_1 is seen to be nothing more than the normalized correlation function of the process. S. O. Rice pointed out that if one applies the Schwarz inequality, the following bound can be established for the expansion coefficients:

(6-92)F $$a_n^2 \leq 1, \text{ for all } n.$$

x_1 and x_2 will, for the remainder of this development, be considered as sample values taken from a pair of random processes $x_1(t)$ and $x_2(t)$ at times t_1 and t_2 respectively. In symbols,

(6-93) $$x_1 = x_1(t_1)$$

$$x_2 = x_2(t_2).$$

6.4.1 ZERO-MEMORY TRANSFORMATIONS

Consider the system shown in Figure 6-4. $H[x(t)]$ is a zero-memory transformation acting on the process $x(t)$.

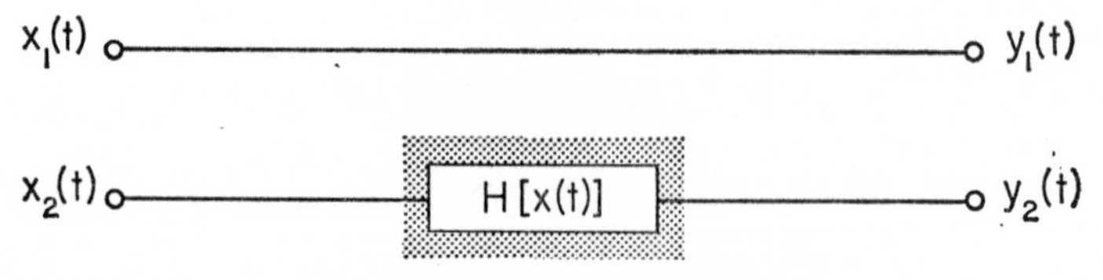

Figure 6-4. Zero Memory Device

The covariance function of the output signals is

$$\psi_{12}(t_1, t_2) = E\{[y_1(t_1) - E\{y_1(t_1)\}][y_2(t_2) - E\{y_2(t_2)\}]\}$$
$$= E\{[x_1 - \mu_1][H(x_2) - E\{H(x_2)\}]\}$$
$$= \iint [x_1 - \mu_1][H(x_2) - E\{H(x_2)\}]f(x_1, x_2)\, dx_1\, dx_2. \tag{6-94}$$

Insert Eqs. (6-90) in Eq. (6-94);

$$\psi_{12}(t_1, t_2) = \sigma_1 \iint \theta_{11}(x_1)[H(x_2) - E\{H(x_2)\}]f(x_1, x_2)\, dx_1\, dx_2. \tag{6-95}$$

As a means to an end, assume that $H(x)$ is restricted so that it can be adequately represented in terms of a series of the orthonormal polynomials $\theta_{2n}(x_2)$. This being assumed, write

$$H(x_2) = \sum_{m=0}^{\infty} C_m \theta_{2m}(x_2), \tag{6-96}$$

where the expansion coefficients are

$$C_m = \int H(x_2) f_2(x_2) \theta_{2m}(x_2)\, dx_2. \tag{6-97}$$

From Eq. (6-90), $\theta_{20}(x_2) = 1$, hence

$$C_0 = \int H(x_2) f_2(x_2) = E\{H(x_2)\}. \tag{6-98}$$

Therefore,

$$H(x_2) - E\{H(x_2)\} = \sum_{m=1}^{\infty} C_m \theta_{2m}(x_2). \tag{6-99}$$

Combine Eqs. (6-99) and (6-95);

$$\psi_{12}(t_1, t_2) = \sigma_1 \iint \theta_{11}(x_1) \left[\sum_{m=1}^{\infty} C_m \theta_{2m}(x_2) \right] f(x_1, x_2)\, dx_1\, dx_2. \tag{6-100}$$

Now insert Eq. (6-83) in (6-100) and apply the orthogonality conditions. The result is

$$\psi_{12}(t_1, t_2) = \sigma_1 \iint \theta_{11}(x_1) f(x_2) \sum_{m=1}^{\infty} \sum_{n=0}^{\infty} C_m a_n \theta_{1m}(x_1) \theta_{2m}(x_2)\, dx_1\, dx_2$$
$$= \sigma_1 a_1 C_1. \tag{6-101)F$$

But from Eq. (6-91), we note that

$$a_1 = \frac{E\{(x_1 - \mu_1)(x_2 - \mu_2)\}}{\sigma_1 \sigma_2} = \frac{R_{12}(t_1, t_2)}{\sigma_1 \sigma_2}. \tag{6-102)F$$

Thus Eq. (6-101) can be written as

$$\psi_{12}(t_1, t_2) = C R_{12}(t_1, t_2), \tag{6-103)F$$

when

$$C = C(t_2) = \int H(x_2) \frac{(x_2 - \mu_2)}{\sigma_2^2} dx_2. \tag{6-104)F}$$

For stationary time series and zero memory devices, Eq. (6-103) can be written simply as

$$\psi_{12}(\tau) = CR_{12}(\tau). \tag{6-105)F}$$

This reduces to Bussgang's result [57] if $x_1(t) = x_2(t)$. The result is a little more general in that Bussgang based his proof on the hypothesis of an original Gaussian process. Equation (6-105), states that for distributions of class F, if one signal is amplitude distorted in a zero-memory device, then the cross-correlation function after the distortion is proportional to the cross-correlation function before distortion.

6.4.2 CONDITIONAL EXPECTATIONS

For a distribution belonging to the class F, Eq. (6-85) can be applied to a conditional frequency function for x_2 given x_1 in the form

$$f(x_2|x_1) = \frac{f(x_1, x_2)}{f_1(x_1)} = f_2(x_2) \sum_{n=0}^{\infty} a_n\theta_{1n}(x_1)\theta_{2n}(x_2). \tag{6-106)F}$$

Thus, by analogy we can write

$$\begin{aligned} E\{\theta_{2m}(x_2)|x_1\} &= \int \theta_{2m}(x_2)f_2(x_2) \sum_{n=0}^{\infty} a_n\theta_{1n}(x_1)\theta_{2n}(x_2)\, dx_2 \\ &= a_m\theta_{1m}(x_1). \end{aligned} \tag{6-107)F}$$

Now let $m = 1$ and apply Eqs. (6-90) and (6-91). Equation (6-107) becomes

$$E\left\{\frac{x_2 - \mu_2}{\sigma_2} \Big| x_1\right\} = \rho(t_1, t_2) \frac{x_1 - \mu_1}{\sigma_1}. \tag{6-108)F}$$

For the special situation which $x_1(t) = x_2(t)$ and $x_1(t)$ is a stationary stochastic process with normalized correlation function $\rho(\tau)$, Eq. (6-108) reduces to

$$E\{x_2 - \mu_2|x_1\} = \rho(\tau)\cdot(x_1 - \mu_1), \tag{6-109)F}$$

where $\tau = t_2 - t_1$.

6.4.3 RELATION OF EXPANSION TO AN INTEGRAL EQUATION

Suppose that $f(x_1, x_2)$ is assumed to be a symmetric joint frequency function. That is

$$f(x_1, x_2) = f(x_2, x_1). \tag{6-110}$$

This being so, we can also write Eq. (6-85) as

$$f(x_1, x_2) = f(x_1)f(x_2) \sum_{n=0}^{\infty} a_n\theta_n(x_1)\theta_n(x_2). \tag{6-111)F}$$

Multiply both sides by $\theta_m(x_2)$ and integrate with respect to x_2. Because of the orthogonality property, the result is

$$\int f(x_1, x_2)\theta_m(x_2)\,dx_2 = a_m f(x_1)\theta_m(x_1). \tag{6-112)F}$$

This can be written in the equivalent form

$$\int \frac{f(x_1, x_2)}{\sqrt{f(x_1)f(x_2)}}\left[\theta_m(x_2)\sqrt{f(x_2)}\right] dx_2 = a_m\left[\theta_m(x_1)\sqrt{f(x_1)}\right]. \tag{6-113)F}$$

Equation (6-113) can be placed in the standard form of a linear homogeneous equation

$$\int k(x_1, x_2)\Phi_m(x_2)\,dx_2 = \lambda_m\Phi_m(x_1), \tag{6-114)F}$$

by making the identifications

$$\begin{aligned} k(x_1, x_2) &= f(x_1, x_2)[f(x_1)f(x_2)]^{-1/2} \\ \Phi_m(x) &= \theta_m(x)[f(x_1)]^{1/2} \\ \lambda_m &= a_m. \end{aligned} \tag{6-115)F}$$

From the definition of Eq. (6-82) it follows that

$$\int \Phi_m(x)\Phi_n(x)\,dx = \int f(x)\theta_m(x)\theta_n(x)\,dx = \delta_{mn}. \tag{6-116)F}$$

Thus the Φ_m defined by Eq. (6-115) are normalized orthogonal eigenfunctions of the linear homogeneous integral equation, Eq. (6-114), having λ_m as the corresponding eigenvalues.

If it can be demonstrated that the set of eigenfunctions defined by Eq. (6-115) are complete, one would have the equivalence between the expansion of Eq. (6-111) and the Mercer expansion

$$k(x_1, x_2) = \sum_{n=0}^{\infty} \lambda_n\Phi_n(x_1)\Phi_n(x_2). \tag{6-117}$$

Because of the difficulties encountered in trying to justify the Mercer expansion, Barrett and Lampard point out that the integral equation approach does not seem to be a suitable starting point for approximating the frequency functions for noise theory applications.

6.4.4 *EXAMPLE OF THE EXPANSION*

One of the examples given by Barrett and Lampard will be used to illustrate an application of the theory.

The joint Gaussian frequency function is

$$f(x_1, x_2) = \frac{(1 - \rho^2)^{-1/2}}{2\pi\sigma^2} \exp\left\{-\frac{1}{2}\left[\frac{x_1^2 + x_2^2 - 2\rho x_1 x_2}{\sigma^2(1 - \rho^2)}\right]\right\}, \tag{6-118}$$

with corresponding first-order frequency function

$$f(x) = \frac{1}{\sigma\sqrt{2\pi}} \exp\left(-\frac{x^2}{2\sigma^2}\right). \tag{6-119}$$

We will require Mehler's expansion, [58].

$$(1 - u^2)^{-1/2} \exp\left\{-\frac{1}{2}\left[\frac{u^2(x_1^2 + x_2^2) - 2u x_1 x_2}{1 - u^2}\right]\right\} = \sum_{n=0}^{\infty} \frac{H_n(x_1)H_n(x_2)}{n!}, \tag{6-120}$$

where $H_n(x)$ is the Hermite polynomial of order n. Insert Eq. (6-120) in Eq. (6-118);

$$f(x_1, x_2) = \frac{1}{2\pi\sigma^2} \exp\left\{-\frac{1}{2\sigma^2}(x_1^2 + x_2^2)\right\} \sum_{n=0}^{\infty} \rho^n \frac{H_n(x_1/\sigma)H_n(x_2/\sigma)}{n!}. \tag{6-121}$$

Because the Hermite polynomials satisfy the orthogonality condition

$$\frac{1}{\sqrt{2\pi}} \int_{-\infty}^{\infty} e^{-x^2/2} H_m(x)H_n(x)\, dx = \delta_{mn} n!, \tag{6-122}$$

Eq. (6-121) can be written in the standard form

$$f(x_1, x_2) = f(x_1)f(x_2) \sum_{n=0}^{\infty} a_n \theta_n(x_1)\theta_n(x_2), \tag{6-123)F$$

where

$$\theta_n(x) = \frac{H_n(x)}{(n!)^{1/2}} \tag{6-124}$$

$$a_n = f^n.$$

Thus, it has been shown that the joint Gaussian frequency function is a member of class F functions.

6.5 WIENER'S METHOD

Most of the techniques for nonlinear transformations of random processes break down if an arbitrary linear filter follows the nonlinear circuit element and is allowed to react on the nonlinear device. As amply demonstrated in Chapter 4, the exact solution for a square law device followed by a linear filter is exceedingly difficult even for the case of an isolated filter. If the filter is not isolated, the solution techniques simply are not applicable.

N. Wiener, [59, 60] gave a solution for a very general class of nonlinear devices followed by an interacting filter. This technique is still relatively unknown and has been seldom used. His basic method is very general and could be used for the square law device to obtain an approximate solution without the mathematical difficulties inherent in solving an integral or differential equation. However, the principal application of Wiener's approach is to situations of interaction between the nonlinear device and linear filters.

The procedure is to solve for the signal across a nonlinear device in terms of the input random process and then to find statistical averages, on the assumption that the current-voltage characteristic and the system transfer functions are known quantities.

6.5.1 COEFFICIENTS FOR NONLINEAR SYSTEM

The general class of systems for which the discussion is applicable is shown in Figure 6-5.

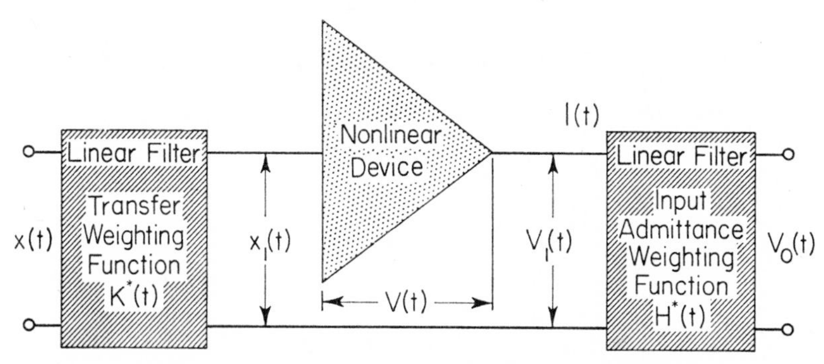

Figure 6-5. Nonlinear Device with Interacting Filters

Suppose, at first, that the input filter is electrically isolated from the remainder of the network. Later, by employing a network theorem, the case of complete interaction will be treated by a simple analogue of the isolated situation.

The input filter is assumed to be linear with a transfer weighting function $K^*(t)$. Hence the output of this filter is

$$X_1(t) = \int_{-\infty}^{\infty} K^*(\tau)X(t-\tau)\,d\tau \tag{6-125}$$

where

$$K^*(\tau) = 0, \qquad \tau < 0. \tag{6-126}$$

Noting this restriction, all integrals are over the range $(-\infty, \infty)$ and integration limits will not be written.

The nonlinear device is restricted to the class for which the current through it can be expressed as a power series of the impressed voltage. The amount of labor required to apply the results of the Wiener method is directly related to the rapidity with which the power series converges.

Let the current be represented by the series

$$I(t) = \sum_n a_n V^n(t). \tag{6-127}$$

If $H^*(t)$ is the input admittance weighting function of the output filter, the current across the input terminals of the output filter is

$$I(t) = \int H^*(\tau) V_1(t - \tau)\, d\tau \tag{6-128}$$

$$H^*(\tau) = 0, \qquad \tau < 0.$$

Because of the series network configuration, Eqs. (6-127) and (6-128) may be equated;

$$\sum_n a_n V^n(t) = \int H^*(\tau)[X_1(t - \tau) - V(t - \tau)]\, d\tau. \tag{6-129}$$

The output voltage, $V_0(t)$, can be computed from $V_1(t)$ if the transfer function of the output filter is given. This is a straightforward calculation and will not be discussed.

The immediate problem is to solve Eqs. (6-129) and (6-125) for $V(t)$ in terms of the input process. For this step, assume that $V(t)$ can be represented by the series form:

(6-130)

$$\begin{aligned} V(t) = Q_0^* &+ \int Q_1^*(\tau_1) X(t - \tau_1)\, d\tau_1 \\ &+ \iint Q_2^*(\tau_1, \tau_2) X(t - \tau_1) X(t - \tau_2)\, d\tau_1\, d\tau_2 \\ &+ \iiint Q_3^*(\tau_1, \tau_2, \tau_3) X(t - \tau_1) X(t - \tau_2) X(t - \tau_3)\, d\tau_1\, d\tau_2\, d\tau_3 + \cdots. \end{aligned}$$

This series representation is fundamental to the Wiener technique because it explicitly relates the input voltage to the voltage across the nonlinear device. For convenience, it is desirable to assume $E\{x(t)\} = 0$. It then follows that $Q_0^* = 0$, since it has been tacitly assumed that the nonlinear device is a passive circuit element.

Equation (6-130) is now substituted in Eq. (6-129) and linear terms equated to linear terms, etc. In this fashion, the function Q_n^* can be evaluated in terms of the nonlinear characteristics and the input and output filter responses. The linear and quadratic terms will be examined in detail. These will establish and illustrate the procedure used to evaluate the higher order terms.

Equating linear terms,

(6-131)

$$a_1 \int Q_1^*(\tau_1)X(t-\tau_1)\,d\tau_1 + \int H^*(\tau) \int Q_1^*(\beta)X(t-\tau-\beta)\,d\beta\,d\tau = \int H^*(\tau) \int K^*(\beta)X(t-\tau-\beta)\,d\beta\,d\tau.$$

In the last two integrals, make the change of variables

(6-132)
$$\tau_1 = \tau + \beta$$
$$\phi = \beta.$$

Then

(6-133)

$$a_1 \int Q_1^*(\tau_1)X(t-\tau_1)\,d\tau_1 + \iint H^*(\tau_1-\phi)Q_1^*(\phi)X(t-\tau_1)\,d\phi\,d\tau_1 = \iint H^*(\tau_1-\phi)K^*(\phi)X(t-\tau_1)\,d\phi\,d\tau_1.$$

This equation has a solution if

(6-134)
$$a_1Q_1^*(\tau_1) + \int H^*(\tau_1-\phi)Q_1^*(\phi)\,d\phi = \int H^*(\tau_1-\phi)K^*(\phi)\,d\phi.$$

Each of the weighting functions is assumed to possess a Fourier transform. A typical example is the transform pair:

(6-135)
$$K^*(t) = \frac{1}{2\pi}\int K(\omega)e^{i\omega t}\,d\omega$$
$$K(\omega) = \int K^*(t)e^{-i\omega t}\,dt.$$

Equation (6-134) can be solved by simply taking the Fourier transform of each term. Denoting the transform of each function by removing the asterisk, the solution for Q_1 is

(6-136)
$$Q_1(\omega) = \frac{H(\omega)K(\omega)}{a_1 + H(\omega)}.$$

If the input filter were removed from the circuit, Eq. (6-136) would be obtained with $K(\omega)$ equal to unity.

Now equate the second degree terms;

(6-137)

$$a_1 \iint Q_2^*(\tau_1,\tau_2)X(t-\tau_1)X(t-\tau_2)\,d\tau_1\,d\tau_2 + a_2\left[\int Q_1^*(\tau_1)X(t-\tau_1)\,d\tau_1\right]^2 + \int H^*(\tau) \iint Q_2^*(\beta_1,\beta_2)X(t-\tau-\beta_1)X(t-\tau-\beta_2)\,d\beta_1\,d\beta_2\,d\tau = 0.$$

After making a change of variables, it is found that Eq. (6-137) will have a solution if

$$a_2Q_1^*(\tau_1)Q_1^*(\tau_2) + a_1Q_2^*(\tau_1, \tau_2) + \int H^*(\tau)Q_2^*(\tau_1 - \tau, \tau_2 - \tau)\, d\tau = 0. \tag{6-138}$$

A solution is obtained by once more taking the Fourier transform of each member of this equation. The solution is

$$Q_2(\omega_1, \omega_2) = \frac{-a_2Q_1(\omega_1)Q_1(\omega_2)}{a_1 + H(\omega_1 + \omega_2)}. \tag{6-139}$$

The same general procedure is used to evaluate as many of the Q_n as are necessary to provide the degree of accuracy required in the solution of any specific applied problems. Several of these coefficients are listed in Table 6-1.

TABLE 6-1

Recurrence Relations for Coefficients Q_n

$$Q_1(\omega_1) = \frac{H(\omega_1)K(\omega_1)}{a_1 + H(\omega_1)}$$

$$Q_2(\omega_1, \omega_2) = \frac{-1}{a_1 + H(\omega_1 + \omega_2)} \{a_2Q_1(\omega_1)Q_1(\omega_2)\}$$

$$Q_3(\omega_1, \omega_2, \omega_3) = \frac{-1}{a_1 + H(\omega_1 + \omega_2 + \omega_3)} \{a_3Q_1(\omega_1)Q_1(\omega_2)Q_1(\omega_3) + 2a_2Q_1(\omega_1)Q_2(\omega_2, \omega_3)\}$$

$$\begin{aligned} Q_4(\omega_1, \omega_2, \omega_3, \omega_4) = \frac{-1}{a_1 + H(\omega_1 + \omega_2 + \omega_3 + \omega_4)} &\{a_4Q_1(\omega_1)Q_1(\omega_2)Q_1(\omega_3)Q_1(\omega_4) \\ &+ 3a_3Q_1(\omega_1)Q_1(\omega_2)Q_2(\omega_3, \omega_4) + 2a_2Q_1(\omega_1)Q_3(\omega_2, \omega_3, \omega_4) \\ &+ a_2Q_2(\omega_1, \omega_2)Q_2(\omega_3, \omega_4)\} \end{aligned}$$

$$\begin{aligned} Q_5(\omega_1, \omega_2, \omega_3, \omega_4, \omega_5) = \frac{-1}{a_1 + H(\omega_1 + \omega_2 + \omega_3 + \omega_4 + \omega_5)} &\{a_5Q_1(\omega_1)Q_1(\omega_2)Q_1(\omega_3)Q_1(\omega_4)Q_1(\omega_5) \\ &+ 4a_4Q_1(\omega_1)Q_1(\omega_2)Q_1(\omega_3)Q_2(\omega_4, \omega_5) + 3a_3Q_1(\omega_1)Q_1(\omega_2)Q_3(\omega_3, \omega_4, \omega_5) \\ &+ 3a_3Q_1(\omega_1)Q_2(\omega_2, \omega_3)Q_2(\omega_4, \omega_5) + 2a_2Q_1(\omega_1)Q_4(\omega_2, \omega_3, \omega_4, \omega_5) \\ &+ 2a_2Q_2(\omega_1, \omega_2)Q_3(\omega_3, \omega_4, \omega_5)\} \end{aligned}$$

6.5.2 *RANDOM INPUT PROCESSES*

Up to this stage in the development, no special properties were required for the input signal $X(t)$; in fact $X(t)$ need not be a random process. To cover many cases of practical interest as well as to formulate a set of explicit relations, we will now assume that $X(t)$ is a stationary ergodic Gaussian process. With this assumption, in theory it is possible to obtain all the statistical information concerning the output voltage to any desired degree of accuracy. The formal procedure is illustrated by the evaluation of $E\{V(t)\}$.

From Eq. (6-130), after interchanging the orders of integration,

$$E\{V(t)\} = \int Q_1^*(\tau_1)E\{X(t-\tau_1)\}\,d\tau_1 \tag{6-140}$$

$$+ \iint Q_2^*(\tau_1,\tau_2)E\{X(t-\tau_1)X(t-\tau_2)\}\,d\tau_1\,d\tau_2$$

$$+ \iiint Q_3^*(\tau_1,\tau_2,\tau_3)E\{X(t-\tau_1)X(t-\tau_2)X(t-\tau_3)\}\,d\tau_1\,d\tau_2\,d\tau_3 + \cdots.$$

We now require a property of Gaussian correlated variates with zero means. It is known that

$$E\{X_1X_2\ldots X_n\} = 0 \qquad \text{if } n \text{ is odd,} \tag{6-141}$$

$$E\{X_1X_2\ldots X_n\} = \Sigma\,\Pi\,R_{jk}R_{lm}\ldots R_{qr} \qquad \text{for } n \text{ even,}$$

where $R(t_j - t_k) = R_{jk} = E\{X_j - X_k\}$. The summation is taken over all partitions of $X_1X_2\ldots X_n$ into distinct pairs and the product is taken over all pairs in each partition. The total number of terms is $\dfrac{n!}{\left(\frac{n}{2}\right)!\,2^{n/2}}$.

With the aid of Eq. (6-141), the terms in Eq. (6-140) can be evaluated. First notice that all the odd power terms will vanish. Consider the two-dimensional term and define

$$M_2 = \iint Q_2^*(\tau_1,\tau_2)E\{X(t-\tau_1)X(t-\tau_2)\}\,d\tau_1\,d\tau_2 \tag{6-142}$$

$$= \iint Q_2^*(\tau_1,\tau_2)R(\tau_2-\tau_1)\,d\tau_1\,d\tau_2.$$

Make the change of variables

$$u = \tau_2 - \tau_1$$

$$\phi = \tau_1;$$

then since Q_2^* has a Fourier transform, we can write

$$M_2 = \frac{1}{(2\pi)^2}\underbrace{\int\cdots\int}_{4} Q_2(\omega,\lambda)e^{i\lambda u}e^{i\phi(\omega+\lambda)}R(u)\,d\phi\,du\,d\omega\,d\lambda. \tag{6-143}$$

Integrate with respect to ϕ,

$$M_2 = \frac{1}{(2\pi)^2}\iiint Q_2(\omega,\lambda)e^{i\lambda u}R(u)2\pi\,\delta(\omega+\lambda)\,du\,d\omega\,d\lambda \tag{6-144}$$

$$= \frac{1}{2\pi}\iint Q_2(\omega,-\omega)e^{-i\omega u}R(u)\,du\,d\omega.$$

The power spectral density function, $W(\omega)$, of the original process, $X(t)$, is simply the Fourier transform of its correlation function, $R(u)$. Noting this, Eq. (6-144) reduces to

(6-145)
$$M_2 = \frac{1}{2\pi} \int Q_2(\omega, -\omega) W(\omega) \, d\omega.$$

Using Table 6-1, it is possible to calculate M_2 for almost any physical system.

The next higher order term in the representation for $E\{V(t)\}$ is treated in a similar fashion. Let

(6-146)
$$M_4 = \underbrace{\int \cdots \int}_{4} Q_4^*(\tau_1, \tau_2, \tau_3, \tau_4)$$
$$E\{X(t - \tau_1)X(t - \tau_2)X(t - \tau_3)X(t - \tau_4)\} \, d\tau_1 \, d\tau_2 \, d\tau_3 \, d\tau_4.$$

Applying Eq. (6-141),

(6-147)
$$M_4 = \underbrace{\int \cdots \int}_{4} Q_4^*(\tau_1, \tau_2, \tau_3, \tau_4)[R(\tau_2 - \tau_1)R(\tau_4 - \tau_3)$$
$$+ R(\tau_3 - \tau_1)R(\tau_4 - \tau_2) + R(\tau_4 - \tau_1)R(\tau_3 - \tau_2)] \, d\tau_1 \, d\tau_2 \, d\tau_3 \, d\tau_4.$$

The result, after the same sort of manipulations used for M_2, is

(6-148)
$$M_4 = \frac{1}{(2\pi)^2} \iint W(\omega_1)W(\omega_2)[Q_4(\omega_1, -\omega_1, \omega_2, -\omega_2)$$
$$+ Q_4(\omega_1, \omega_2, -\omega_1, -\omega_2) + Q_4(\omega_1, \omega_2, -\omega_2, -\omega_1)] \, d\omega_1 \, d\omega_2.$$

Proceeding in the general fashion just illustrated, $E\{V(t)\}$ can be computed for any desired number of terms in its series representation. From these results, the expected value of the output process is found from the relation

(6-149)
$$E\{V_1(t)\} = E\{X_1(t) - V(t)\}$$
$$= E\{X_1(t)\} - E\{V(t)\}.$$

$E\{X_1(t)\}$ is obtained from Eq. (6-125),

(6-150)
$$E\{X_1(t)\} = E\left\{\int K^*(\tau)X(t - \tau) \, d\tau\right\}$$
$$= \int K^*(\tau)E\{X(t - \tau)\} \, d\tau.$$

But by assumption $E\{X(t)\} = 0$, therefore

(6-151)
$$E\{V_1(t)\} = -E\{V(t)\}.$$

The higher moments of the output signal can be computed in a similar fashion and the procedure involves no real difficulties; only patience is required.

6.5.3 CORRELATION FUNCTION

If one is interested in the correlation function of the output process following the nonlinear device, it is necessary to evaluate the expected value

(6-152)

$$\begin{aligned} E\{V_1(t)V_1(t-\tau)\} &= E\{[X_1(t) - V(t)][X_1(t-\tau) - V(t-\tau)]\} \\ &= E\{X_1(t)X_1(t-\tau)\} + E\{V(t)V(t-\tau)\} \\ &\qquad - E\{X_1(t)V(t-\tau)\} - E\{V(t)X_1(t-\tau)\}. \end{aligned}$$

Each of the terms in Eq. (6-152) will be evaluated in turn. From Eq. (6-125) it follows that

$$E\{X_1(t)X_1(t-\tau)\} = \iint K^*(\tau_1)K^*(\tau_2)R(\tau + \tau_2 - \tau_1)\, d\tau_1\, d\tau_2. \tag{6-153}$$

After making a change of variable and using the Fourier transform of each function,

$$E\{X_1(t)X_1(t-\tau)\} = \frac{1}{2\pi}\int K(\omega)K(-\omega)W(\omega)e^{i\omega\tau}\, d\omega. \tag{6-154}$$

The second term in the decomposition of the correlation function displayed in Eq. (6-152) is found to any desired degree of accuracy by employing Eq. (6-130). Keeping in mind that the expected value $E\{X_1X_2 \ldots X_n\}$ vanishes for n odd, some of the leading terms of the expansion are

(6-155)

$$\begin{aligned} E\{V(t)V(t-\tau)\} = E\Big\{ &\iint Q_1^*(\tau_1)Q_1^*(\tau_2)X(t-\tau_1)X(t-\tau_2)\, d\tau_1\, d\tau_2 \\ &+ 2\underbrace{\int \ldots \int}_{4} Q_1^*(\tau_1)Q_3^*(\tau_2, \tau_3, \tau_4) \\ &\qquad X(t-\tau_1)X(t-\tau-\tau_2)X(t-\tau-\tau_3) \\ &\qquad X(t-\tau-\tau_4)\, d\tau_1\, d\tau_2\, d\tau_3\, d\tau_4 \\ &+ \ldots \text{(linear} \times \text{higher odd powers)} \\ &+ \underbrace{\int \ldots \int}_{4} Q_2^*(\tau_1, \tau_2)Q_2^*(\tau_3, \tau_4)X(t-\tau_1)X(t-\tau_2) \\ &\qquad X(t-\tau-\tau_3)X(t-\tau-\tau_4)\, d\tau_1\, d\tau_2\, d\tau_3\, d\tau_4 \\ &+ \ldots \text{(quadratic} \times \text{higher even powers)} \\ &+ \underbrace{\int \ldots \int}_{6} Q_3^*(\tau_1, \tau_2, \tau_3)Q_3^*(\tau_4, \tau_5, \tau_6) \\ &\qquad X(t-\tau_1)X(t-\tau_2)X(t-\tau_3)X(t-\tau-\tau_4) \\ &\qquad X(t-\tau-\tau_5)X(t-\tau-\tau_6)\, d\tau_1\, d\tau_2\, d\tau_3\, d\tau_4\, d\tau_5\, d\tau_6 \\ &+ \ldots \text{(tertiary} \times \text{higher odd powers)} \\ &+ \ldots \text{(higher order terms)}\Big\}. \end{aligned}$$

The individual terms in Eq. (6-155) can all be evaluated by applying the general procedures already described.

The third term in Eq. (6-152) is treated in a similar fashion. Finally, consider the last term in Eq. (6-152). Retaining only the nonvanishing terms

(6-156)

$$E\{X_1(t)V(t-\tau)\} = E\left\{\iint Q_1^*(\tau_1)K^*(\tau_2)X(t-\tau_2)X(t-\tau-\tau_1)\,d\tau_1\,d\tau_2\right\} + E\Big\{\underbrace{\int\cdots\int}_{4} Q_3^*(\tau_1,\tau_2,\tau_3)K^*(\tau_4)\, X(t-\tau_1)X(t-\tau-\tau_2)X(t-\tau-\tau_3)\, X(t-\tau-\tau_4)\,d\tau_1\,d\tau_2\,d\tau_3\,d\tau_4\Big\} + \cdots .$$

After a few standard manipulations, we find

(6-157)

$$E\{X_1(t)V(t-\tau)\} = \frac{1}{2\pi}\int W(\omega)Q_1(\omega)K(-\omega)e^{i\omega\tau}\,d\omega + \frac{1}{(2\pi)^2}\iint W(\omega_1)W(\omega_2)\exp\,[i(\omega_1+\omega_2)\tau]K(\omega_1) [Q_3(-\omega_1,\omega_2,-\omega_2) + Q_3(\omega_2,-\omega_1,-\omega_2) + Q_3(\omega_2,-\omega_2,\omega_1)]\,d\omega_1\,d\omega_2 + \cdots]$$

6.5.4 INPUT LOADING

We are now in a position to return to the original network in which the input filter is not isolated from the nonlinear device and the output filter. By applying Thevenin's theorem, the network of Figure 6-5 can be replaced by that shown in Figure 6-6. In Figure 6-6,

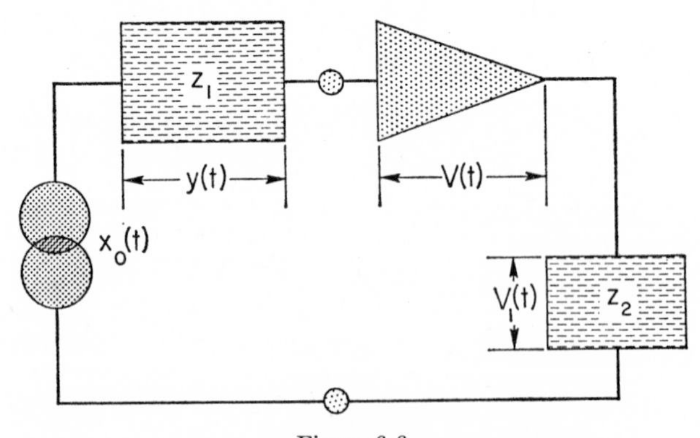

Figure 6-6.

(6-158) Z_1 = short circuit impedance of the input filter looking into its output terminals

$$X_0(t) = \int K^*(\tau)X(t - \tau)\,d\tau$$

$X_0(t)$ = open circuit output voltage of filter.

A trivial rearrangement of the series network leads to the equivalent circuit illustrated in Figure 6-7. This circuit can be analyzed using exactly

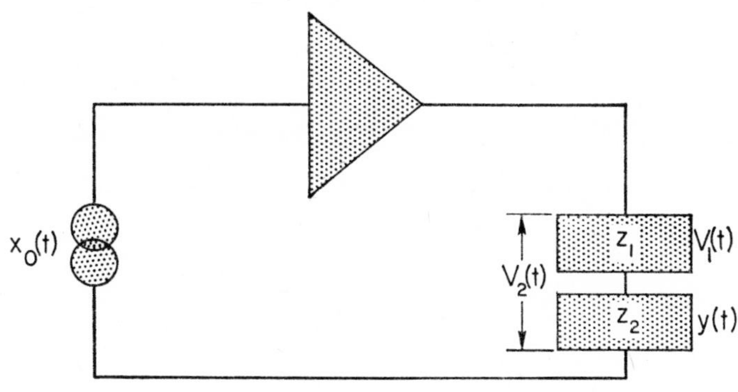

Figure 6-7.

the same procedures already outlined. A simple approach is to use the relations previously developed by an analogy using the following replacement of variables:

(6-159)

OLD	*NEW*	
$X_1(t)$	$X_0(t)$	
$V_1(t)$	$V_2(t)$	
$I(t)$	$I(t)$	
$V(t)$	$V(t)$	
$H^*(t)$	$L^*(t)$,	combined admittance weighting function of Z_1 and Z_2 in series.

The table of coefficients, Table 6-1, is modified by replacing $H(\omega)$ by $L(\omega)$ and letting $K(\omega) = 1$. In this manner, the problem of finding the statistical moments of the signal process $V(t)$, is immediately solved from the solution of the simpler case of an isolated input filter. The last step is to find the statistical properties of the new output signal, $V_1(t)$.

Let $M^*(t)$ be the impedance weighting function of the output filter. Then

(6-160)
$$V_1(t) = \int M^*(\tau)I(t - \tau)\,d\tau$$

$$M^*(\tau) = 0, \qquad \tau < 0.$$

Using Eq. (6-127),

$$V_1(t) = \Sigma\, a_n \int M^*(\tau)V^n(t-\tau)\,d\tau. \tag{6-161}$$

Therefore, the statistics of $V_1(t)$ are obtained from those of $V(t)$ which are already known, or by using the methods indicated for computing higher order statistics.

An interesting expression can be obtained for the signal $X_1(t)$ defined in Figure 6-5. Expressed in terms of the transformed circuit illustrated in Figure 6-7,

$$\begin{aligned} X_1(t) &= X_0(t) - y(t) \\ &= \int K^*(\tau)X(t-\tau)\,d\tau - \int N^*(\tau)I(t-\tau)\,d\tau \\ N^*(t) &= 0, \qquad t < 0, \end{aligned} \tag{6-162}$$

where $N^*(t)$ is the impedance weighting function of Z_1. Thus,

$$X_1(t) = \int K^*(\tau)X(t-\tau)\,d\tau - \sum_n a_n \int N^*(\tau)V^n(t-\tau)\,d\tau. \tag{6-163}$$

The first term on the right-side of Eq. (6-163) is that for the output voltage if the nonlinear device were absent. Therefore, the second term contains the interaction of the nonlinear circuit on the filter output voltage.

6.5.5 DUAL ANALYSIS

Some nonlinear devices may have characteristics which are more conveniently described by a relation dual to Eq. (6-127), that is

$$V(t) = \sum_n b_n I^n(t). \tag{6-164}$$

The same general method already described can again be applied. We eliminate $V(t)$ with the relation

$$V(t) = X_1(t) - \int B^*(\tau)I(t-\tau)\,d\tau. \tag{6-165}$$

and assume a representation for $I(t)$ similar to Eq. (6-130). $B^*(\tau)$ is the input impedance weighting function of the output filter. Let

$$I(t) = \int q_1^*(\tau_1)X(t-\tau_1)\,d\tau_1 + \iint q_2^*(\tau_1, \tau_2)X(t-\tau_1)X(t-\tau_2)\,d\tau_1\,d\tau_2 + \cdots. \tag{6-166}$$

The foundation for the dual analysis is completely contained in Eqs. (6-164), (6-165), and (6-166). The development exactly parallels that presented in the preceding paragraphs.

6.6 REPRESENTATION OF NONLINEAR OPERATORS

In Sec. 6.5, a method for dealing with nonlinear transformations of random processes was formulated by representing the nonlinearity as an infinite series. This technique can be extended to a general series technique for treating nonlinear zero-memory transformations by representing their transfer characteristics by a series of uncorrelated functions. Zadeh has made an extensive survey of this approach and some of the important and interesting aspects of his investigation follow, [62].

Not all nonlinear transformations can be represented by a series of uncorrelated functions. Therefore, at the outset we will restrict ourselves to the class of nonlinear operators F, which are sufficiently well-behaved to permit the following expansion of the type used by Volterra, [63]

(6-167)

$$F[x(t)] = K_0 + \int_0^\infty K_1(\tau_1)x(t-\tau_1)\,d\tau_1 + \iint_0^\infty K_2(\tau_1,\tau_2)x(t-\tau_1)x(t-\tau_2)\,d\tau_1\,d\tau_2 + \iiint_0^\infty K_3(\tau_1,\tau_2,\tau_3)x(t-\tau_1)x(t-\tau_2)x(t-\tau_3)\,d\tau_1\,d\tau_2\,d\tau_3 + \ldots,$$

where the constant K_0 and the kernel functions $K_1, K_2, K_3, \ldots$ are analogous to the coefficients of the expansion of an n-place function in an n-variate power series. Obviously, the Wiener method of Sec. 6.5 is an example of the application of an operator of class F.

6.6.1 ORTHOGONAL REPRESENTATIONS

For many applications, the Volterra expansion, Eq. (6-167) is much too general. Instead of the general series, we will sacrifice some generality and construct simpler representations based upon an orthogonality restriction. Let $\{x(t)\}$ be an ergodic random process and let $F_1[x(t)]$ and $F_2[x(t)]$ be two functionals defined on the set $\{x(t)\}$. Then, F_1 and F_2 are said to be orthogonal functionals relative to the process $\{x(t)\}$ if

(6-168) $$E\{F_1[x(t)]F_2[x(t)]\} = 0.$$

However, if F_1 and F_2 are nonlinear operators, the condition given in Eq. (6-168) is not sufficiently strong for our purpose. Instead, we will define operators F_1 and F_2 to be orthogonal relative to $\{x(t)\}$, if and only if for all τ,

(6-169) $$E\{F_1[x(t)]F_2[x(t-\tau)]\} = 0.$$

This last definition is motivated by the requirement that a series expansion is to be introduced using uncorrelated expansion functions.

An example of this type of orthogonal representations was given by Martin and Cameron, [64]. Let $\{x(t)\}$ be a *white* Gaussian process with unity variance, and let $\{\alpha_n(t)\}$, $n = 1, 2, \ldots$ be a complete orthonormal set of real functions. Now define a set of random variables by the relation

$$y_n = \int_0^1 \alpha_n(t)x(t)\,dt. \tag{6-170}$$

Because of the linearity property of an integral, the $\{y_n\}$ will form a set of Gaussian distributed independent random variables. These can be considered to be the coordinates of $x(t)$ with respect to the basis $\{\alpha_n(t)\}$. In this manner, a nonlinear functional defined on the set $\{x(t)\}$, $0 \leq t \leq 1$, can be represented as the limit as $N \rightarrow \infty$ of an ordinary function of the form $f(y_1, y_2, \ldots, y_N)$.

Because of the similarity of the Gaussian frequency function to a Hermite polynomial, we define

$$\Phi_{mn}[x(t)] = H_m(y_n) \tag{6-171}$$

and

$$\Phi_{m_1,m_2,\ldots,m_n}[x(t)] = H_{m_1}(y_1)H_{m_2}(y_2)\ldots H_{m_n(y_n)}, \tag{6-172}$$

where $H_m(u)$ denotes the normalized Hermite polynomial which can be defined by the representation

$$H_m(u) = (-1)^m 2^{-m/2}(m!)e^{u^2}\frac{d^m}{du^m}(e^{-u^2}). \tag{6-173}$$

Since the y_n are independent and normally distributed with zero mean and unit variance, the Φ functionals form an orthonormal set in the sense that

$$E\{\Phi_{m_1,m_2,\ldots,m_n}[x(t)]\Phi_{k_1,k_2,\ldots,k_n}[x(t)]\} = \delta_{m_1k_1}\delta_{m_2k_2}\ldots\delta_{m_nk_n}. \tag{6-174}$$

Therefore, f can be represented formally by the series

$$f(y_1, y_2, \ldots, y_N) = \sum_{m_1=0}^{\infty}\ldots\sum_{m_N=0}^{\infty} A_{m_1,m_2,\ldots,m_N}\Phi_{m_1,m_2,\ldots,m_N}[x(t)], \tag{6-175}$$

where, because of Eq. (6-174), the coefficients are determined from

$$A_{m_1,m_2,\ldots,m_N} = E\{f(y_1, y_2, \ldots, y_N)\Phi_{m_1,m_2,\ldots,m_N}[x(t)]\}. \tag{6-176}$$

Combining these results, the representation of the operator F for this example, assumes the explicit form

$$F[x(t)] = \lim_{N\rightarrow\infty}\sum_{m_1=0}^{\infty}\ldots\sum_{m_N=0}^{\infty} A_{m_1,m_2,\ldots,m_N}H_{m_1}\left[\int_0^1 \alpha_1(t)x(t)\,dt\right]\ldots H_{m_N}\left[\int_0^1 \alpha_N(t)x(t)\,dt\right]\Big\}. \tag{6-177}$$

Cameron and Martin proved that for any functional of class $L_2(C)$, the series in Eq. (6-177), converges to $F[x(t)]$ in the $L_2(C)$ sense. A functional is said to be of class $L_2(C)$ if

$$E\{F^2[x(t)]\} < \infty. \tag{6-178}$$

A variant of the representation in Eq. (6-167) was developed by Barrett, [65] in which the multinomial terms are grouped in such a way as to form n-variate Hermite polynomials. These polynomials are defined as follows, [66]:

$$\begin{aligned} H^{(0)} &= 1 \\ H_i^{(1)} &= x_i \\ H_{ij}^{(2)} &= x_i x_j - \delta_{ij} \\ H_{ijk}^{(3)} &= x_i x_j x_k - (x_i \delta_{jk} + x_j \delta_{ki} + x_k \delta_{ij}) \\ H_{ijkq}^{(4)} &= x_i x_j x_k x_q - (x_i x_j \delta_{kq} + x_j x_k \delta_{qi} \\ &\qquad + x_k x_q \delta_{ij} + x_q x_i \delta_{jk} + x_i x_k \delta_{jq} + x_j x_q \delta_{ki}) \\ &\qquad + (\delta_{ij}\delta_{kq} + \delta_{ik}\delta_{jq} + \delta_{iq}\delta_{jk}) \\ &\qquad \cdots \end{aligned} \tag{6-179}$$

Zadeh pointed out that the polynomials in Eq. (6-179) can be expressed as products of ordinary Hermite polynomials. For example:

$$\begin{aligned} H_{112}^{(3)} &= x_1^3 x_2 - x_2 = H_2(x_1)H_1(x_2), \\ H_{1123}^{(4)} &= x_1^2 x_2 x_3 - x_2 x_3 = H_1(x_2)H_2(x_1)H_1(x_3). \end{aligned} \tag{6-180}$$

If the x_i are normally distributed random variables with zero mean value and unity variance, then the n-variate Hermite polynomials obey the orthogonality relation

$$E\{H_{i_1 i_2 \ldots i_m}^{(m)} H_{i_1 i_2 \ldots i_n}^{(m)}\} = \delta_{ij}^m, \tag{6-181}$$

where $i = (i_1, \ldots, i_m)$, $j = (j_1, \ldots, j_m)$ and δ_{ij}^m is equal to the sum of all distinct products of n Kronecker deltas of the form $\delta_{i_\mu j_\nu}$ such that all i_μ and j_ν occur only once in each product. As an illustration,

$$\delta_{ij}^2 = \delta_{i_1 j_1}\delta_{i_2 j_2} + \delta_{i_1 j_2}\delta_{i_2 j_1} \tag{6-182}$$

and

$$E\{H_{12}^{(2)} H_{21}^{(2)}\} = 1 \tag{6-183}$$

$$E\{H_{11}^{(2)} H_{11}^{(2)}\} = 2. \tag{6-184}$$

If we identify x_i with the process $x(t_i)$ and δ_{ij} is replaced by $\delta(t_i - t_j)$, then these polynomials can be used to represent nonlinear operators acting upon a random process. Applying these identifications, we obtain the functional Hermite polynomials:

(6-185)
$$\begin{aligned} H^{(0)} &= 1 \\ H^{(1)}[x(t_i)] &= x(t_i) \\ H^{(2)}[x(t_i), x(t_j)] &= x(t_i)x(t_j) - \delta(t_i - t_j) \\ H^{(3)}[x(t_i), x(t_j), x(t_k)] &= x(t_i)x(t_j)x(t_k) - [x(t_i)\delta(t_j - t_k) \\ &\quad + x(t_j)\delta(t_k - t_i) + x(t_k)\delta(t_i - t_j)]. \end{aligned}$$

These polynomials will be orthonormal in the sense of Eq. (6-181) if the random process is white noise with unit variance; or more precisely is normally distributed with zero mean and unit variance. Thus

(6-186)
$$E\{[H^{(m)}[x(t_1), \ldots, x(t_m)]][H^{(n)}[x(t_1 + \tau), \ldots, x(t_n + \tau)]]\} = 0$$
$$\text{for all } \tau(m \neq n) = \delta_{ij}^{n}(m = n).$$

Barrett showed that these polynomials can readily be extended to Gaussian processes with arbitrary spectrum by replacing $\delta(t_\nu - t_\mu)$ with $E\{x(t_\mu)x(t_\nu)\}$. His representation results from grouping the terms in Eq. (6-167) into the functional Hermite polynomials defined by Eq. (6-185) with $\delta(t_\nu - t_\mu)$ replaced by

(6-187)
$$\phi(t_\nu - t_\mu) = E\{x(t_\mu)x(t_\nu)\}.$$

When this is done, the operator representation becomes

(6-188)
$$\begin{aligned} F[x(t)] = k_0 &+ \int_0^\infty k_1(\tau_1)H^{(1)}[x(t - \tau_1)]\, d\tau_1 \\ &+ \iint_0^\infty k_2(\tau_1, \tau_2)H^{(2)}[x(t - \tau_1), x(t - \tau_2)]\, d\tau_1\, d\tau_2 \\ &+ \iiint_0^\infty k_3(\tau_1, \tau_2, \tau_3)H^{(3)}[x(t - \tau_1), x(t - \tau_2), x(t - \tau_3)]\, d\tau_1\, d\tau_2\, d\tau_3 \\ &+ \cdots. \end{aligned}$$

6.6.2 EXAMPLE

The general expression for the operator representation in Eq. (6-188) is very cumbersome except for some particular subclasses of nonlinear operators. As an illustrative example, consider the particular class of operators which can be characterized by the relation

(6-189)
$$F[x(t)] = \sum_{n=0}^{\infty} \int_0^\infty k_n(\tau)\theta_n[x(t - \tau)]\, d\tau,$$

where

(6-190) $$E\{\theta_n[x(t - \tau_1)\theta_m[x(t - \tau_2)]\} = \delta_{mn}.$$

If $x(t_i)$ is a Gaussian process with zero mean value, one can show that

(6-191) $$\theta_n(x) = H_n\left(\frac{x}{\sigma}\right),$$

where

$$\sigma^2 = E\{x^2(t)\}.$$

Let $x_1 = x(t - \tau_1)$ and $x_2 = x(t - \tau_2)$. The joint frequency function is

(6-192) $$f(x_1, x_2) = \frac{1}{2\pi\sigma^2}\frac{1}{\sqrt{1-\rho^2}} \exp\left\{-\frac{1}{2}\left[\frac{x_1^2 + x_2^2 - 2\rho x_1 x_2}{\sigma^2(1-\rho^2)}\right]\right\},$$

where

$$\rho = \frac{\phi(\tau_1 - \tau_2)}{\sigma^2}.$$

Using Mehler's expansion, Eq. (6-120),

(6-193)
$$f(x_1, x_2) = \frac{1}{2\pi\sigma^2} \exp\left\{-\frac{1}{2}\left[\frac{x_1^2 + x_2^2}{\sigma^2}\right]\right\} \sum_{n=0}^{\infty} \frac{\rho^n}{n!} H_n\left(\frac{x_1}{\sigma}\right) H_n\left(\frac{x_2}{\sigma}\right).$$

Therefore,

(6-194) $$E\{\theta_n(x_1)\theta_m(x_2)\} = \iint_{-\infty}^{\infty} f(x_1, x_2)\theta_n(x_1)\theta_m(x_2)\, dx_1\, dx_2$$

$$= n!\left[\frac{\phi(\tau_1 - \tau_2)}{\sigma^2}\right]^n \delta_{mn}.$$

Hence, for a Gaussian process, Eq. (6-189) becomes

(6-195) $$F[x(t)] = \sum_{n=0}^{\infty} \int_0^{\infty} k_n(\tau) H_n\left[\frac{x(t-\tau)}{\sigma}\right] d\tau.$$

Using Eq. (6-194) the correlation function after the operator action assumes the form

(6-196) $$\psi(\tau) = \sum_{n=0}^{\infty} n! \iint_0^{\infty} k_n(\tau_1)k_n(\tau_2)\left[\frac{\phi(\tau_1 - \tau_2)}{\sigma^2}\right]^n d\tau_1\, d\tau_2.$$

6.7 REPRESENTATION OF A FREQUENCY FUNCTION BY ITS MOMENTS

An implicit assumption underlying much of the development in this chapter, is that a probability frequency function is determined by its moments. It is exactly this assumption that leads us to evaluating moments when the nature of the nonlinear operator does not permit an analytic determination of the complete frequency function of the transformed random process. In practice, it is virtually impossible to compute, or even measure, more than the first few moments of a random process. The inaccuracies in approximations, or measurements, grow with the order of the moment so that the process cannot be extended very far before very little confidence can be attached to the values of the higher order moments.

For these reasons, it is necessary to examine just what frequency function is determined if only the moments m_1 to m_n are available. Clavier has considered this problem and has constructed a frequency function corresponding to the first n moments when one does not have *a priori* knowledge of the general characteristics of the true frequency function from which the samples were selected, [67].

Corresponding to a frequency function $f(x)$, we have the characteristic function defined by the Fourier transform relation

(6-197) $$g(z) = \int_{-\infty}^{\infty} f(x) \exp(-2\pi i z x)\, dx.$$

The moment generating property of the characteristic function is displayed by the process of expanding the exponential function and integrating termwise to obtain the series

(6-198) $$g(z) = \sum_{q=0}^{\infty} (-2\pi i)^q \frac{z^q m_q}{q!},$$

where

(6-199) $$m_q = E\{x^q\}.$$

Suppose that only the first n moments are known, then corresponding to Eq. (6-198) we have a function defined as

(6-200) $$g'(z) = \sum_{q=0}^{n} (-2\pi i)^q \frac{z^q m_q}{q!}.$$

This is a convergent series because it is the sum of a finite number of terms. However, its Fourier transform is

(6-201) $$f'(x) = \sum_{q=0}^{n} \frac{(-1)^q}{q!} \delta_0^q(x) m_q,$$

where $\delta_0^q(x)$ is the q'th derivative of the Dirac-delta function evaluated at $x = 0$. Obviously the function $f'(x)$ has the same first n moments as $f(x)$, but the two functions are not identical. Without prior knowledge concerning $f(x)$, the best that one can do is to modify $f'(x)$ so that at least it has the properties of a frequency function.

At this point we require a property of distribution functions. Schwartz [68], has shown that the series

(6-202) $$\delta_{xi}(\phi) = \phi(x_i) = \sum_q \frac{x_i^q}{q!} \phi^n(0),$$

is well defined nearly everywhere if the ϕ are functions of class D. Based upon Eq. (6-202), we can justify the series expansion for the Dirac-delta function

$$\delta_{x_i}(x) = \sum_q \frac{(-1)^q}{q!} x_i^q \delta_0^n(x). \tag{6-203}$$

Assume that we can represent $f'(x)$ in the form

$$f'(x) = \sum_i a_i \delta_{x_i}(x), \qquad a_i \geq 0. \tag{6-204}$$

Insert the series of Eq. (6-203) in Eq. (6-204);

$$f'(x) = \sum_{q=0}^{n} \frac{(-1)^q}{q} \left(\sum_i a_i x_i^q\right) \delta_0^n(x). \tag{6-205}$$

Comparing Eq. (6-205) with Eq. (6-201) indicates that

$$m_q = \sum_i a_i x_i^q. \tag{6-206}$$

Thus if Eq. (6-206) is satisfied, the function $f'(x)$ defined in Eq. (6-204) has the same moments as the true frequency function $f(x)$. Since all the $a_i \geq 0$, $f'(x)$ is now a frequency function for which the first n moments are the same as those for the frequency function $f(x)$.

The solution of Eq. (6-206) for a finite number of moments has a well-defined solution for any chosen set of x_i. The condition that $a_i \geq 0$ will restrict the possible choices of x_i.

7 TECHNIQUES USING DIFFERENTIAL AND INTEGRAL EQUATIONS

7.1 GENERAL REMARKS

It is apparent that no general analytical technique exists for studying the action of a general nonlinear transformation on an arbitrary random process. Methods were illustrated in previous chapters that are applicable to rather severely restricted classes of nonlinear operations. Even with these restrictions it was often necessary to limit the techniques to transformations of a Gaussian process. To a large extent, these limitations were often imposed on the techniques described in Chapter 6 where one is satisfied with merely seeking a fair approximation to the statistical properties of a transformed random process.

Although it is a painfully slow procedure, progress in the study of nonlinear transformations of random processes usually occurs by choosing a particular type of process $x(t)$ and a transformation V such that the combination is amenable to analysis. In this chapter we will develop a systematic procedure for studying functionals of the type

$$m(s, t; \omega) = \int_s^t V[x(\tau, \omega), \tau]\, d\tau, \tag{7-1}$$

where $x(\tau, \omega)$ is a stochastic process and V is a function with certain prescribed regularity properties. V may be linear or nonlinear. The general problem is to study the statistical properties of $m(s, t)$ for various classes of stochastic processes and functions V.

The form of Eq. (7-1) is not completely arbitrary and is chosen because there is sufficient theoretical and applied interest in the statistical characteristics of $m(s, t)$ to warrant intensive study of this functional. Functionals of stochastic processes arise in many situations where one might least expect them as well as in other cases that obviously should involve functionals. A few examples will illustrate the practical motivation for studying processes expressed in the form of Eq. (7-1).

(i) *Limit theorems and functionals*

Let $x_1, x_2, \ldots$ be independent random variables with zero mean value, unit variance and such that the central limit theorem is applicable. Let $S_k = x_1 + x_2 + \ldots + x_k$ and let $V(x)$ be a non-negative function of the real variable x. Furthermore, let $x(\tau)$, $[x(0) = 0, 0 \leq \tau < \infty]$ be the Wiener process (Gaussian process with independent increments). Under comparatively mild restrictions on $V(x)$ it can be shown that

$$\lim_{n\to\infty} \text{Prob}\left\{\frac{1}{n}\sum_{k\leq nt} V\left(\frac{S_k}{\sqrt{n}}\right) < a\right\} = \text{Prob}\left\{\int_0^t V[x(\tau)]\,d\tau < a\right\}. \tag{7-2}$$

In this fashion it is evident that limiting distributions can be obtained by calculating the probability distributions of Wiener functionals.

(ii) *Random walk with absorbing barriers*

Let $x_1, x_2, \ldots$ be independent random variables with zero mean value, unit variance and such that the central limit theorem is applicable. Let $S_k = x_1 + \ldots + x_k$ and let $x(\tau)$, $[x(0) = 0, 0 \leq \tau < \infty]$ be the Wiener process. Then it can be shown that regardless of the distribution of the x_i,

$$\lim_{n\to\infty} \text{Prob}\left\{\max_{1\leq k\leq nt} S_k < a\sqrt{n}\right\} = \text{Prob}\left\{\max_{0\leq\tau\leq t} x(\tau) < a\right\}. \tag{7-3}$$

Moreover, the right-hand side can be calculated by noting that

$$\text{Prob}\left\{\max_{0\leq\tau\leq t} x(\tau) < a\right\} = \lim_{z\to\infty} E\left\{\exp\left[-z\int_0^t V_a[x(\tau)]\,d\tau\right]\right\}, \tag{7-4}$$

where

$$V_a = \begin{cases} 0, & x < a \\ 1, & x > a. \end{cases} \tag{7-5}$$

If in Eq. (7-4) we define

$$V_{a,b} = \begin{cases} 0; & -b < x < a, \quad a > 0, \quad b > 0 \\ 1; & x < -b, \quad x > a, \end{cases} \tag{7-6}$$

then the left side becomes

$$\text{Prob}\left\{-b \leq \min_{0\leq\tau\leq t} x(\tau) \leq \max_{0\leq\tau\leq t} x(\tau) < a\right\}. \tag{7-7}$$

Equation (7-5) corresponds to the random walk with one absorbing barrier while Eq. (7-6) corresponds to the random walk with two absorbing barriers.

(iii) *Nonlinear noise problems*

Functionals of the canonical form, Eq. (7-1), are frequently encountered in the study of physical systems which are either perturbed by noise or which have random processes as input signals. For example, suppose that the input signal is a random process, $x(t)$. This signal is then operated upon by a device with a transform characteristic V. The output of this device, $V[x(t)]$, is finally processed by a linear filter having a weighting function $k(t)$. The resulting signal, $m(t)$ is thus related to the original process by the functional

$$m(t) = \int_{-\infty}^{t} k(t - \tau) V[x(\tau)] \, d\tau. \tag{7-8}$$

(iv) *Estimate of distributions from finite samples*

In Eq. (7-1) define

$$V(x, t) = \begin{cases} 1, & x \text{ in } D \\ 0, & x \text{ not in } D. \end{cases} \tag{7-9}$$

With this function, $m(s, t)$ becomes the fraction of time that x spends in the domain D during an interval $(t - s)$. The probability that x will be in D for this finite interval is $m(s, t)/(t - s)$. Hence the distribution of $m(s, t)$ is important as an estimate of the accuracy for which the probability of $x(t)$ can be obtained from finite samples.

(v) *Distribution of spectral components*

The problem of determining the distribution of spectral components obtained from measurements on a finite sample size also can be formulated in terms of the canonical functional $m(s, t)$. Suppose that $\psi_1(\tau)$, $\psi_2(\tau)$, . . . , $\psi_q(\tau)$ are given functions; for example, trigonometric functions. The characteristic function for the joint distribution of the Fourier coefficients is

$$E\left\{\exp\left[i \sum_{k=1}^{q} z_k \int_s^t \psi_k(\tau) x(\tau) \, d\tau\right]\right\}. \tag{7-10}$$

Now if one chooses

$$V[x(\tau), \tau] = \frac{x(\tau)}{z} \sum_{k=1}^{q} z_k \psi_k(\tau), \tag{7-11}$$

then the characteristic function

$$E\left\{\exp\left[iz \int_s^t V[x(\tau), \tau] \, d\tau\right]\right\} \tag{7-12}$$

is also the characteristic function for the joint distribution of the Fourier coefficients.

No systematic theory or technique exists for investigating functionals of the canonical type defined by Eq. (7-1) when both $x(t)$ and V are completely arbitrary. However several important inroads on the general problem have been made by restricting the generality of the random process and the operator V so that they combine in a manner that is amenable to analysis.

One of the first solutions for a particular case of Eq. (7-1) was obtained by Kac and Siegert (Chapter 4) for the situation in which $x(t)$ is a Gaussian process and $V(x) = x^2$. They obtained the solution for the distribution of

$$m(t) = \int_0^t k(\tau)x^2(\tau)\, d\tau \tag{7-13}$$

employing an analysis technique which requires finding the eigenfunctions generated by an integral equation. Using a related method Kac [69], computed the characteristic function of m, where

$$m = \int_0^1 |x(\tau)|\, d\tau, \tag{7-14}$$

and $x(\tau)$ is the Wiener process.

Two systematic studies have been made of functionals, Eq. (7-1), for $x(t)$ being a Wiener process. One approach has been through procedures developed by Cameron and Martin, [70]. An example of their work was given in Chapter 6. Another approach introduced by Kac [71, 72, 73] appears easier to apply to mathematical and physical problems and lends itself by generalization to other than Wiener processes.

For the Wiener process in one dimension, Kac formulated differential and integral equations for the characteristic function of Eq. (7-1). Later, Rosenblatt, [74], extended Kac's results to the n-dimensional Wiener process and materially relaxed the restrictions imposed on the function V.

Darling and Siegert, [75, 76, 77, 78], recognized that the underlying basis for the success of Kac's method was that the Wiener process is a Markov process. They were able to extend Kac's theory to include a quite general n-dimensional Markov process. Almost simultaneously, Fortet [79] made a similar extension to Markov processes. One form of the extended theory is presented in the next section using formal operations with no attempt to rigorously argue the fine points in the mathematical development, [80].

7.2 INTEGRAL EQUATION

Because of the widespread applications to physical systems, the analysis will be developed for a functional of the form

$$m(t) = \int_{-\infty}^t K(t-\tau)V[x(\tau)]\, d\tau. \tag{7-15}$$

Let $x(t) = [x_1(t), x_2(t), \ldots, x_n(t)]$ be a vector Markov process taking values in the Euclidean n-space. The transition probability between states of the process $x(t)$ is denoted by

$$\text{Prob}\ \{x(t) \leqslant \eta | x(s) = \xi\} = P(\xi, s; \eta, t), \tag{7-16}$$

where the vector relation $\xi < \eta$ implies the component relation $\xi_i < \eta_i$. It is convenient to denote the lower limit of integration in Eq. (7-15) by the letter s.

Define an auxiliary function R by the relation

$$R(\xi, s; \eta, t|z) = E\left\{\exp\,[izm(s, t)] \left| \begin{matrix} x(t) \leqslant \eta \\ x(s) = \xi \end{matrix} \right.\right\} P(\xi, s; \eta, t). \tag{7-17}$$

R is seen to be the product of a conditional expectation and a transition probability function. Although it isn't necessary to the basic theory, we will assume that the transition probability P has a corresponding density p and R also has a corresponding density function r. Thus, we can write

$$r(\xi, s; \eta, t|z) = E\left\{\exp\,[izm(s, t)] \left| \begin{matrix} x(t) = \eta \\ x(s) = \xi \end{matrix} \right.\right\} p(\xi, s; \eta, t). \tag{7-18}$$

If the auxiliary function r can be determined, then its knowledge is equivalent to having the characteristic function q of the process $m(s, t)$, [76]. For example:

(i) If the initial and end conditions $x(s) = \xi$ and $x(t) = \eta$ are fixed, then

$$q = r/p. \tag{7-19}$$

(ii) If the initial condition $x(s) = \xi$ is fixed but not the end point, then

$$q(t|z) = \int_{-\infty}^{\infty} r(\xi, s; \eta, t|z)\, d\eta. \tag{7-20}$$

(iii) If neither end point is fixed, then

$$q(t|z) = \int_{-\infty}^{\infty} \int_{-\infty}^{\infty} p(\xi, s) r(\xi, s, \eta, t|z)\, dz\, d\eta, \tag{7-21}$$

where $p(\xi, s)$ is the probability density of the random variable $x(s) = \xi$.

Note that for integrals involving vectors, such as Eqs. (7-20) and (7-21), the notation used is $d\eta = d\eta_1\, d\eta_2 \ldots d\eta_n$ with the integration extending over the Euclidean n-space.

Starting with the following identity, an integral equation will be derived which is satisfied by the auxiliary density function, r.

$$\exp\,\{izm(s, t)\} \equiv 1 + \int_s^t \frac{\partial}{\partial u} \exp\,\{izm(s, u)\}\, du. \tag{7-22}$$

Replace $-\infty$ by s and substitute Eq. (7-14) in Eq. (7-22), then

$$e^{izm(s,t)} = 1 + iz \int_s^t K(0)V[x(u)]e^{izm(s,u)}\,du + iz \int_s^t e^{izm(s,u)}\,du \int_s^u \frac{\partial}{\partial u} K(u-\tau)V[x(\tau)]\,d\tau. \tag{7-23}$$

Take the expected value of both sides conditioned by fixed initial and end points for the process $x(t)$, and then multiply the result by the transition probability density of the process $x(t)$. Applying the definition of Eq. (7-18), one finds that

$$\begin{aligned} r(\xi, s; \eta, t|z) &= p(\xi, s; \eta, t) \\ &+ iz \int_s^t K(0)E\left\{V[x(u)]e^{izm(s,u)} \middle| \begin{matrix} x(t) = \eta \\ x(s) = \xi \end{matrix}\right\} p(\xi, s; \eta, t)\,du \\ &+ iz \int_s^t du \int_s^u \frac{\partial}{\partial u} K(u-\tau)E\left\{V[x(\tau)]e^{izm(s,u)} \middle| \begin{matrix} x(t) = \eta \\ x(s) = \xi \end{matrix}\right\} p(\xi, s; \eta, t)\,d\tau. \end{aligned} \tag{7-24}$$

Equation (7-24) can be simplified if we restrict ourselves to the weighting function

$$K(u-\tau) = Ae^{-a(u-\tau)}, \tag{7-25}$$

where A and a are constants. The same techniques that follow can readily be extended to situations in which the true weighting function can be approximated by sums of exponentials, or

$$K(t) = \sum_j A_j e^{-a_j t}. \tag{7-26}$$

At this stage, introduce the Chapman-Kolmogorov equation for the transition probability density:

$$p(\xi, s; \eta, t) = \int_{-\infty}^{\infty} p(\xi, s, \beta, u)p(\beta, u; \eta, t)\,d\beta. \tag{7-27}$$

Insert Eqs. (7-25) and (7-26) into Eq. (7-24) and use the definition of Eq. (7-18) to formulate the desired integral equation for r;

$$\begin{aligned} r(\xi, s; \eta, t|z) &= p(\xi, s; \eta, t) \\ &+ izA \int_s^t \int_{-\infty}^{\infty} V(\beta)r(\xi, s; \beta, u|z)p(\beta, u; \eta, t)\,d\beta\,du \\ &- za \int_s^t \int_{-\infty}^{\infty} \frac{\partial}{\partial z} r(\xi, s; \beta, u|z)p(\beta, u; \eta, t)\,d\beta\,du. \end{aligned} \tag{7-28}$$

Equation (7-28) is called the *forward* equation because it is a function of η, t with $t < s$. ξ, s, z are merely parametric quantities in the equation. A similar *backward* equation can also be formulated for r as a function of ξ and s.

7.3 PARTIAL DIFFERENTIAL EQUATION

The integral equation formulation for the auxiliary density r, Eq. (7-28), is valid under rather mild conditions on the process $x(t)$ and the operator V. In spite of this, in practice it is usually very difficult to find solutions of Eq. (7-28). By placing a few additional restrictions on the Markov process and the operator V, it is possible to reduce Eq. (7-28) to a more tractable form. We first consider the result of restricting the process.

Let the process $x(t)$ be Markovian having a probability density function satisfying the Fokker-Planck equation:

$$\left[L^* - \frac{\partial}{\partial t}\right] p(\xi, s; \eta, t) = 0, \tag{7-29}$$

where L^* is a differential operator. For example, if $x(t)$ is a one-dimensional process, we might choose L^* such that

$$\frac{1}{2}\frac{\partial^2 p}{\partial \eta^2} + [b_0(t) + b_1(t)\eta]\frac{\partial p}{\partial \eta} + b_1(t)p = \frac{\partial}{\partial t} p(\xi, s; \eta, t). \tag{7-30}$$

This choice encompasses two important Gaussian Markov processes. The transition probability density for the Wiener-Lévy process satisfies Eq. (7-30) with the values $b_0 = b_1 = 0$. The density function for the Uhlenbeck-Ornstein process results from the values $b = 0$, $b_1 =$ constant.

Assuming that all the required derivatives of r exist, apply Eq. (7-29) to Eq. (7-28). The result of the differential operators is

$$\frac{1}{2}\frac{\partial^2 r}{\partial \eta^2} + (b_0 + b_1\eta)\frac{\partial r}{\partial \eta} + b_1 r + izAVr - za\frac{\partial r}{\partial z} = \frac{\partial}{\partial t} r(\xi, s; \eta, t|z). \tag{7-31}$$

This equation can be transformed to the standard parabolic form by introducing the change of variables

$$\zeta = ze^{at}. \tag{7-32}$$

The new equation can be written as

$$\frac{1}{2}\frac{\partial^2 v}{\partial \eta^2} + (b_0 + b_1\eta)\frac{\partial v}{\partial \eta} + b_1 v + i\zeta Ae^{-at}Vv = \frac{\partial}{\partial t} v(\xi, s; \eta, t|\zeta). \tag{7-33}$$

r was replaced by v to emphasize the change of independent variables (η, t, z) to (η, t, ζ). Equation (7-33) is called the *reduced* equation corresponding to the *determining* equation, Eq. (7-31).

A slight extension of the preceding development can be made to formulate a differential equation applicable when the input signal $x(t)$ is a multi-dimensional process. This extension has been made and an n-dimensional problem has been solved using the resulting differential equation, [74].

7.4 SOLUTION OF THE REDUCED EQUATION

Further progress is possible by turning our attention to the operator V. If V is piecewise quadratic, then a general solution technique can be developed for the reduced equation, [80]. Suppose that V can be written in the form

(7-34) $$V(\eta) = h_0[\eta] + h_1[\eta]\eta + h_2[\eta]\eta^2,$$

where $h_i[\eta]$ is a constant, or zero, for specified values of η. Although this is a fairly severe restriction on V, many common physical devices are included in this class of piecewise quadratic functions. If $h_0 = h_1 = 0$ for all values of η, we have the simple signal squarer. The half-wave squarer is obtained by letting $h_0 = h_1 = 0$ and $h_2 = 0$ for $\eta < 0$; $h_2 =$ constant for $\eta > 0$. Obviously h_i can be defined so that fairly complicated nonlinear operators can be closely represented by segments of quadratic functions.

The solution of the reduced equation will be obtained when V is quadratic; that is, the h_i have constant values for all η. Assume that the differential equation, Eq. (7-33), is satisfied by a solution having the following exponential form:

(7-35) $$V(\xi, s; \eta, t|\zeta) = \exp\,[a_2(t)\eta^2 + 2a_1(t)\eta + a_0(t)].$$

Substitute Eq. (7-35) in Eq. (7-33) and equate coefficients of powers of η. A system of three ordinary differential equations is obtained. These are,

(7-36) $$\frac{d\alpha_2}{dt} = 2\alpha_2^2 + 2\alpha_2 b_1 + i\zeta A e^{-at} h_2$$

(7-37) $$\frac{d\alpha_1}{dt} = 2\alpha_1\alpha_2 + \alpha_1 b_1 + \alpha_2 b_0 + \frac{i\zeta}{2} A e^{-at} h_1$$

(7-38) $$\frac{d\alpha_0}{dt} = \alpha_2 + 2\alpha_1^2 + 2b_0\alpha_1 + b_1 + i\zeta A e^{-at} h_0.$$

Several facts should be noted concerning this system of equations. First, the coefficients are functions only of t. Second, Eqs. (7-37) and (7-38) are linear and can be solved by quadratures once a solution for $\alpha_2(t)$ is known from Eq. (7-36). Finally, Eq. (7-36) is the Ricatti differential equation. This equation has been extensively studied and many of the tabulated solutions can often be employed to evaluate $\alpha_2(t)$, [82].

The integration constants for the system of coefficient equations are evaluated after first returning to the original set of variables, (t, η, z). The appropriate boundary conditions for determining the values of these integration constants are

(7-39) $$\lim_{t \to s+} r(\xi, s; \eta, t|z) = \delta(\eta - \xi);$$

$$\lim_{|\eta - \xi| \to \infty} r(\xi, s; \eta, t|z) = 0.$$

Inherent in the form of Eq. (7-36) is the principal reason why the solution technique works for the reduced equation when V is a piecewise quadratic operator. The Ricatti equation exhibits the quadratic nonlinearity in the term α_2^2. If we make the change of variables

$$\alpha_2 = -\frac{1}{2w}\frac{dw}{dt} \tag{7-40}$$

then Eq. (7-36) becomes a linear second order equation,

$$\frac{d^2w}{dt^2} = 2b_1(t)\frac{dw}{dt} + i\,\zeta\,Ae^{-at}h_2 w. \tag{7-41}$$

Essentially, it is this linearizing characteristic of the Ricatti equation which makes the entire solution technique workable. In fact, trying to extend the method to even the form $V = x^3$ produces nothing.

What happens when we have the more general case in which V is piecewise quadratic? If the nonlinearity exhibits a piecewise characteristic, such as the half wave rectifier, the problem can be attacked by first finding the fundamental solution for r using Eq. (7-35) with coefficients satisfying Eqs. (7-36), (7-37), (7-38) and (7-39). Then it is necessary to add other functions so that at all discontinuities $(\eta, t) = (\xi, s)$, the value of r and its first derivative are equal on both sides of the discontinuity. One of the examples will illustrate the procedure.

The technique of obtaining the fundamental solution of Eq. (7-33) is closely related to the work of Dressel, [83], and Husimi, [84].

7.5 MOMENTS

When V is not a piecewise quadratic function, or if the transition probability density does not satisfy the Fokker-Planck equation, it is necessary to return to the integral equation. Following the usual course when complete solutions for the statistics of a process can not be obtained analytically, the next step is to consider formulations for the moments of the process $m(s, t)$. An integral equation can be found for the characteristic function of $m(s, t)$. From the moment generating properties of the characteristic function, an expression will be obtained for the moments of $m(s, t)$.

Repeat the derivation of Sec. 7.5.2 starting with the identity

$$\exp\{izm(s, t)\} \equiv 1 - \int_s^t \frac{\partial}{\partial u}\exp\{izm(u, t)\}\,du. \tag{7-42}$$

The net result is the *backward* integral equation for the auxiliary density function r;

(7-43)
$$r(\xi, s; \eta, t|z) = p(\xi, s; \eta, t) + izA \int_s^t \int_{-\infty}^{\infty} V(\beta)r(\beta, u; \eta, t|z)p(\xi, s; \beta, u)\, d\beta\, du + za \int_s^t \int_{-\infty}^{\infty} \frac{\partial}{\partial z} r(\beta, u; \eta, t|z)p(\xi, s; \beta, u)\, d\beta\, du,$$

where now (η, t, z) are considered as parametric variables. If this equation is integrated over the entire real line with respect to the variable η, the result is an integral equation satisfied by the characteristic function of $m(s, t)$. Thus

(7-44)
$$q(\xi, s; t|z) = 1 + izA \int_s^t \int_{-\infty}^{\infty} V(\beta)q(\beta, u; t|z)p(\xi, s; \beta, u)\, d\beta\, du + za \int_s^t \int_{-\infty}^{\infty} \frac{\partial}{\partial z} q(\beta, u; t|z)p(\xi, s; \beta, u)\, d\beta\, du.$$

Let μ denote the statistical moments of $m(s, t)$; that is

(7-45)
$$\mu_j = E\{m^j(s, t)\}.$$

If $E\{m^n(s, t)\} < \infty$ for some $n > 0$, then for $j \leq n$, the characteristic function can be expanded into a series in the neighborhood of $z = 0$. Hence,

(7-46)
$$q(\xi, s; t|z) = 1 + \sum_{j=1}^{n} \frac{\mu_j(\xi, s; t|z)}{j!} (iz)^j + O(|z|^n).$$

Substitute Eq. (7-46) in Eq. (7-44) and equate like powers of j. One finds that

(7-47)
$$u_j(\xi, s; t|z) = jA \int_s^t \int_{-\infty}^{\infty} V(\beta)\mu_{j-1}(\beta, u; t|z)p(\xi, s; \beta, u)\, d\beta\, du + ja \int_s^t \int_{-\infty}^{\infty} \mu_j(\beta, u; t|z)p(\xi, s; \beta, u)\, d\beta\, du.$$

This integral is to be evaluated in the neighborhood of $z = 0$. If we recall that $\mu_0 = 1$, then it is evident that the first integral on the right hand side is evaluated as a recurrence relation on the moments; therefore, each moment of $m\ (s, t)$ can be found by solving an integral equation which is simpler than either Eq. (7-43) or (7-44). This statement is not meant to imply that it is an easy matter to solve Eq. (7-47) for arbitrary processes $x(t)$ and operators V.

7.6 EXAMPLES

(a) Consider an input Wiener process $x(t)$ which is squared and passed through an isolated single time constant filter, [85]. The output process can be written as

$$m(t) = A \int_{-\infty}^{t} e^{-a(t-\tau)} x^2(\tau)\, d\tau. \tag{7-48}$$

For the stated example, the reduced equation corresponding to Eq. (7-33) is

$$\frac{1}{2}\frac{\partial^2 v}{\partial \eta^2} + i\zeta A e^{-at}\eta^2 v = \frac{\partial v}{\partial t}. \tag{7-49}$$

First, let us investigate the boundary conditions. Following the solution technique, assume a solution of the form

$$v = \exp\,[\alpha_2(t)\eta^2 + 2\alpha_1(t)\eta + \alpha_0(t)], \tag{7-50}$$

subject to the boundary conditions:

(i) When $t \to 0$, $v \to \delta(\eta)$. Thus $\alpha_2 \to \infty$ independently of z, and α_1 and α_0 must be such that

$$\lim_{t\to 0} \text{area } v \text{ (over } \eta) = 1.$$

But symmetry of $\delta\,(\eta)$ also requires that $\alpha_1 \to 0$ as $t \to 0$.

(ii) When $\zeta \to 0$, $v \to p(\eta, t) = (2\pi|t|)^{-1/2} \exp\left(-\frac{1}{2}\frac{\eta^2}{|t|}\right)$.

The coefficient equations for this example are found to be

$$\frac{d\alpha_2}{dt} = 2\alpha_2^2 + i\zeta A e^{-at}, \tag{7-51}$$

$$\frac{d\alpha_1}{dt} = 2\alpha_1\alpha_2, \tag{7-52}$$

$$\frac{d\alpha_0}{dt} = \alpha_2 + 2\alpha_1^2. \tag{7-53}$$

In Eq. (7-51) make the standard change of variable

$$\alpha_2 = -\frac{1}{2w}\frac{dw}{dt}, \tag{7-54}$$

The new equation is

$$\frac{d^2 w}{dt^2} = i\zeta A e^{at} w. \tag{7-55}$$

The general solution of Eq. (7-55) is

$$w(\zeta, u) = c_1(\zeta)J_0(u) + c_2(\zeta)Y_0(u), \tag{7-56}$$

where

$$u = -\frac{2}{a}\sqrt{2i\zeta}\, e^{-at/2}. \tag{7-57}$$

Therefore, from Eqs. (7-54) and (7-56),

$$\alpha_2 = \frac{-\sqrt{i\zeta}\left[c_1(\zeta)J_1\left(-\frac{2}{a}\sqrt{2iZ}\right) + c_2(\zeta)Y_1\left(-\frac{2}{a}\sqrt{2iZ}\right)\right]}{2\left[c_1(\zeta)J_0\left(-\frac{2}{a}\sqrt{2iZ}\right) + c_2(\zeta)Y_0\left(-\frac{2}{a}\sqrt{2iZ}\right)\right]}. \tag{7-58}$$

Now apply boundary condition ii; that is, as $t \to 0$, $\alpha_2 \to \frac{-1}{2|t|} \to \infty$. This will only occur in Eq. (7-58) if when $z \to \zeta$,

$$\frac{c_1(\zeta)}{c_2(\zeta)} = -\frac{Y_0\left(-\frac{2}{a}\sqrt{2i\zeta}\right)}{Y_1\left(-\frac{2}{a}\sqrt{2i\zeta}\right)}. \tag{7-59}$$

Hence, combining some functions of ζ into $f(\zeta)$, we can write

(7-60)

$$w(\zeta, t) = f(\zeta)$$

$$\left[Y_0\left(-\frac{2}{a}\sqrt{2i\zeta}\right)J_0\left(-\frac{2}{a}\sqrt{2iz}\right) - J_0\left(-\frac{2}{a}\sqrt{2i\zeta}\right)Y_0\left(-\frac{2}{a}\sqrt{2iz}\right)\right].$$

Using the first terms of the expansions of Y_0, J_0, Y_1, J_1 about $u = 0$,

$$w \approx f(\zeta)\left[\frac{2}{\pi}\ln\frac{\sqrt{2i\zeta}}{-a} - \frac{2}{\pi}\left(\ln\frac{\sqrt{2i\zeta}}{-a} - \frac{at}{2}\right)\right] = f(\zeta)\cdot\frac{at}{\pi}. \tag{7-61}$$

From boundary condition ii, we infer that as $\zeta \to 0$, $w \to 2\pi t$ since $\alpha_2 = -\frac{1}{2w}\frac{dw}{dt}$. Applying this condition to Eq. (7-61) produces

$$f(\zeta) = \frac{2\pi^2}{a}, \tag{7-62}$$

and

$$w(z, t) = \frac{2\pi^2}{a}\left[Y_0\left(-\frac{2}{a}e^{at/2}\sqrt{2iz}\right)J_0\left(-\frac{2}{a}\sqrt{2iz}\right) - J_0\left(-\frac{2}{a}e^{at/2}\sqrt{2iz}\right)Y_0\left(-\frac{2}{a}\sqrt{2iz}\right)\right]. \tag{7-63}$$

Insert these results in Eq. (7-50) and integrate over all values of η to obtain the characteristic function

$$q(z, t) = \left[-\frac{\pi\sqrt{2iz}}{a}\left\{Y_0\left(-\frac{2}{a}\sqrt{2iz}\,e^{at/2}\right)J_1\left(-\frac{2}{a}\sqrt{2iz}\right) - J_0\left(-\frac{2}{a}\sqrt{2iz}\,e^{at/2}\right)Y_1\left(-\frac{2}{a}\sqrt{2iz}\right)\right\}\right]^{-1/2}. \tag{7-64}$$

(b) The perfect limiter (Chapter 2) serves as an example in which a solution must be found for a piecewise operator. Let

$$m(t) = \int_0^t V[x(\tau)]\,d\tau \tag{7-65}$$

where $x(t)$ is the Wiener process and the operator is

$$V(x) = \begin{cases} 1; & x > 0 \\ 0; & x < 0 \end{cases}. \tag{7-66}$$

Applying the fundamental solution technique to this problem produces the result

$$r(\eta, t|z) = \frac{1}{\sqrt{2\pi t}} e^{-\eta^2/2t} e^{zV(\eta)t}. \tag{7-67}$$

However, because of the piecewise character of V, this solution does not satisfy the boundary conditions at $\eta = 0$. Following standard procedures for this situation occurring in boundary value problems, we consider the modified solution

$$r = \frac{1}{\sqrt{2\pi t}} e^{-\eta^2/2t} e^{zV(\eta)t} + \int_0^t \frac{B_i(\tau)}{\sqrt{2\pi(t-\tau)}} e^{-\eta^2/2(t-\tau)} e^{iz(t-\tau)V} \, d\tau. \tag{7-68}$$

The constants B_i; $i = 1, 2$ are to be adjusted to satisfy the boundary conditions at the discontinuity $\eta = 0$. It is expedient to work with the Laplace transform of Eq. (7-68) rather than with the original functions. In the transformed domain, the boundary conditions are those required to obtain a Green's function solution; namely

$$\hat{r}_+(0+, \lambda) = \hat{r}_-(0-, \lambda) \tag{7-69}$$

and

$$\frac{\partial}{\partial \eta} \hat{r}_+(0+, \lambda) - \frac{\partial}{\partial \eta} \hat{r}_-(0-, \lambda) = -2, \tag{7-70}$$

where

$$\hat{r}(\eta, \lambda) = \int_0^\infty e^{-\lambda t} r(\eta, t) \, dt. \tag{7-71}$$

These conditions lead to

$$B_1(\lambda) = B_2(\lambda) = \frac{\sqrt{\lambda - iz} - \sqrt{\lambda}}{\sqrt{\lambda - iz} + \sqrt{\lambda}}. \tag{7-72}$$

The remainder of the solution is straightforward and it is found that the characteristic function for the output process $m(t)$ is

$$q = \exp\left(-\frac{izt}{2}\right) I_0\left(-\frac{izt}{2}\right). \tag{7-73}$$

Whence, taking the Fourier transform of Eq. (7-73), the probability that $m(t)$ will not exceed σ is

$$\text{Prob}\,\{m\,(t) \leqslant \sigma\} = \frac{2}{\pi} \arcsin \sqrt{\sigma/t}. \tag{7-74}$$

8 SAMPLING AND QUANTIZING

8.1 INTRODUCTION

The operations known as sampling and quantizing have become commonplace in many physical systems. These operations are not confined to random processes, but because of the universal presence of noise, the same operations either inadvertently or deliberately are applied to random processes. Such transformations are sometimes forced by physical limitations such as occur with pulsed radar wherein only sampled information is available from the signal source. Sampling is now an important item in modern communication systems which employ pulse position modulation or pulse width modulation. In a sampled data system, one is generally interested in trying to reconstruct the information that was contained in the original signal from a set of signal samples.

A companion process is that of signal quantizing. Quantizing is usually employed in an attempt to eliminate the infinity of amplitudes represented in a signal process by assigning all amplitudes in a fixed increment to some preassigned signal amplitude. If the signal is perturbed by additive noise, ambiguities will occur in the resultant quantized levels. These ambiguities represent signal processing levels and are themselves a random process.

Process sampling is also an analytic technique often used to replace a random process by a time series having independent increments. This application of a sampled process was used in Sec. 4.9.

8.2 PERIODIC SAMPLED RANDOM PROCESS

Let $Z(t)$ be a stationary random process which will be sampled periodically by a sampling function whose amplitude will be determined by the amplitude of the random process at the moment of sampling. For illustration, suppose $Z(t)$ is a complex-valued process which can be represented by the series.

$$Z(t) = \sum_{n=-\infty}^{\infty} c_n \exp(2\pi i f_n t). \tag{8-1}$$

Since the exact form of the series representation is not too important, other representations such as the stochastic integral representation of a wide sense stationary process, [34], can be used without complicating the development or materially changing the conclusions.

$Z(t)$ is to be sampled periodically by a sample function having a period T_0. Let $t' = kT_0$, $(k = 1, 2, \ldots)$, where k is the largest integer for which $t \geq kT_0$. Denote the time series resulting from the sampling by $H(t)$. Then

$$H(t) = Z(t')g(t - t') \tag{8-2}$$

where $g(t)$ is the sampling function.

If $t = kT_0$, define

$$H(t) = \tfrac{1}{2}[H(t-) + H(t+)]. \tag{8-3}$$

Insert Eq. (8-1) into Eq. (8-2);

$$\begin{aligned} H(t) &= \sum_n c_n \exp(2\pi i f_n t')g(t - t') \\ &= \sum_n c_n \exp(2\pi i f_n t) \exp[-2\pi i f_n(t - t')]g(t - t'). \end{aligned} \tag{8-4}$$

The last two factors in the product are periodic with the same period. Thus they can be represented by the Fourier series

$$\exp(-2\pi i f_n t)g(t) = \sum_{k=-\infty}^{\infty} a_k \exp\left(\frac{2}{T_0}\pi i k t\right), \tag{8-5}$$

where the coefficients are

$$a_k = \frac{1}{T_0}\int_{-T_0/2}^{T_0/2} g(t) \exp[-2\pi i t(f_n + k/T_0)]\, dt. \tag{8-6}$$

Hence, we can write

$$H(t) = \sum_{n,k} c_n \left[\frac{1}{T_0}\int_{-T_0/2}^{T_0/2} g(t) \exp\left[-2\pi i t\left(f_n + \frac{k}{T_0}\right)\right] dt\right] \exp[2\pi t i f(f_n + k/T_0)]. \tag{8-7}$$

As a specific application of the basic relation Eq. (8-7), consider the simple rectangular gating function that is often used in physical systems for signal sampling:

$$g(t) = 1; \qquad |t| \leq s/2 \tag{8-8}$$
$$= 0; \qquad |t| > s/2$$
$$g(t) = g(t + kT_0).$$

With this definition of the sampling function, Eq. (8-7) reduces to

$$H(t) = \sum_{n,k} \frac{c_n s}{T_0} \frac{\sin \pi s(f_n + k/T_0)}{\pi s(f_n + k/T_0)} \exp\,[2\pi i(f_n + k/T_0)t]. \tag{8-9}$$

The covariance function of this sampled process is readily computed to be

$$R(\tau) = \sum_{m,k} \frac{E\{|c_m|^2\}}{T_0^2} \frac{s^2 \sin^2 \pi s(f_m + k/T_0)}{\pi^2 s^2 (f_m + k/T_0)} \exp\,[-2\pi i\tau(f_m + k/T_0)]. \tag{8-10}$$

One observes from the correlation function that the result of periodic sampling is a time series in which all of the original frequency terms have been modified by the addition of k/T_0 ($k = 0, \pm 1, \pm 2, \ldots$); and the amplitudes have been multiplied by a $(\sin x)/x$ factor containing the original frequencies and harmonics of the sampling frequency.

8.3 SAMPLING THEOREM

Frequently one is confronted with a time series which was generated by periodically sampling an original process. It is of practical interest to know under what conditions the samples can be used to reconstruct the original time series. We will first look at this problem of reconstruction in a simple heuristic fashion.

Let $x(t)$ be a time series whose spectral content, $G(f)$, is known to lie entirely within the frequency limits $(-\lambda, \lambda)$. Then we can formally write

$$x(t) = \int_{-\infty}^{\infty} G(f) \exp\,(2\pi ift)\,df = \int_{-\lambda}^{\lambda} G(f) \exp\,(2\pi ift)\,df. \tag{8-11}$$

We can also write

$$G(f) = \sum_{n=-\infty}^{\infty} a_n \exp\,(-in\pi f/\lambda), \tag{8-12}$$

where

$$a_n = \frac{1}{2\lambda} \int_{-\lambda}^{\lambda} G(f) \exp\,(in\pi f/\lambda)\,df. \tag{8-13}$$

Substitute Eq. (8-12) in Eq. (8-13);

$$a_n = \frac{1}{2\lambda}\, x\left(\frac{n}{2\lambda}\right). \tag{8-14}$$

Now insert Eqs. (8-12) and (8-13) into Eq. (8-11). The result is

$$x(t) = \frac{1}{2\lambda}\int_{-\lambda}^{\lambda} \exp(2\pi ift)\left[\sum_{n=-\infty}^{\infty} x\left(\frac{n}{2\lambda}\right)\exp(-in\pi f/\lambda)\right]df \tag{8-15}$$

$$= \frac{1}{2\lambda}\sum_{n=-\infty}^{\infty} x\left(\frac{n}{2\lambda}\right)\int_{-\lambda}^{\lambda}\exp\left[iz\pi f\left(t-\frac{n}{2\lambda}\right)\right]df$$

$$= \sum_{n=-\infty}^{\infty} x\left(\frac{n}{2\lambda}\right)\frac{\sin \pi(2\lambda t - n)}{\pi(2\lambda t - n)}.$$

The inference in this last equation is that if we know $x(t)$ at its sample points $x\left(\frac{n}{2\lambda}\right)$, then the time series can be reconstructed from its sampled values. The fundamental interval $\frac{1}{2\lambda}$ is called the Nyquist interval. For $G(t)$ limited to zero value outside the frequency interval $(-\lambda, \lambda)$, Eq. (8-15) shows that no new information is gained by choosing a sampling period $T_s < \frac{1}{2\lambda}$.

The sampling theorem is nothing more than a theorem concerning the interpolation between periodic sampled amplitudes of a time series. As such, it is preferable to present the theorem in more rigorous form from the point of view of interpolation theory. This approach has been carried through by several investigators; however the work of Jagerman and Fogel [86] motivates the following development.

A few mathematical results and definitions serve as a preliminary to more detailed generalized sampling theorems. Suppose we have a sequence of sampled amplitudes $\{x_n\}$, where for convenience we use the notation $x_i = x(t_i)$. The problem is essentially one of finding a polynomial interpolation function which will pass without error through each of the given sampled points. Alternate approaches, which will not be discussed, would be to find functions which, with suitably defined metrics, pass arbitrarily close to each sample point.

Lagrange, [87], introduced an interpolation polynomial defined as

$$P_n(t) = x_0L_0^n(t) + x_1L_1^n(t) + \ldots + x_nL_n^n(t), \tag{8-16}$$

where the Lagrangian coefficients are

$$L_j^n(t) = \frac{(t-t_0)(t-t_1)\ldots(t-t_{j-1})(t-t_{j+1})\ldots(t-t_n)}{(t_j-t_0)(t_j-t_1)\ldots(t_j-t_{j-1})(t_j-t_{j+1})\ldots(t_j-t_n)}. \tag{8-17}$$

These coefficients have the property that

$$L_j^n(t_i) = \delta_{ij}. \tag{8-18}$$

Thus, at each instant of time, only one term remains in Eq. (8-16) and has a unit coefficient. All other terms will vanish at that instant. Because of this property of the Lagrangian coefficients, the interpolation polynomial P_n will agree exactly with the original process at each of the sampled points. Since P_n is a polynomial of degree n, it is specified by values at $n + 1$ points and will have n zeros, including possible multiple zeros. By this argument it follows that P_n is uniquely defined by the sampled values.

If $x(t)$ is the original time series, the interpolation error is, [88]

$$x(t) - P_n(t) = \frac{x^{(n+1)}(\tau)}{(n+1)!}(t - t_0)(t - t_1)\ldots(t - t_n) \tag{8-19}$$

where

$$\min_j t_j \leq \tau \leq \max_j t_j. \tag{8-20}$$

Equation (8-17) can be reduced to a simpler form by introducing the auxiliary function

$$g_n(t) = (t - t_0)(t - t_1)\ldots(t - t_n). \tag{8-21}$$

Using this function, the Lagrange coefficients can be written as

$$L_j^n(t) = \frac{g_n(t)}{(t - t_j)g_n'(t)}, \tag{8-22}$$

where

$$g_n'(t) = \frac{d}{dt}\, g_n(t). \tag{8-23}$$

In the same fashion, Eq. (8-16) becomes

$$P_n(t) = g_n(t) \sum_{j=0}^{n} \frac{x_j}{(t - t_j)g_n'(t)}. \tag{8-24}$$

The motivation for employing the auxiliary function is to express P_n by a partial fraction expansion. Now replace t by the complex variable z. After making the change of variable, divide Eq. (8-24) by $g_n(z)$ and define

$$\Phi(z) = \frac{P_n(z)}{g_n(z)} = \frac{x_0}{(z - z_0)g_n'(z_0)} + \cdots + \frac{x_n}{(z - z_n)g_n'(z_n)}. \tag{8-25}$$

Note that $g_n(z)$ is an entire function which vanishes at each sample point. Because $P_n(z)$ is also an entire function, $\phi(z)$ is meromorphic and has a simple pole at each sample point.

We now wish to obtain a generalization which holds when the number of sample points becomes infinite. For this generalization it is necessary to choose an entire function which has zeros at a countable infinity of equidistant points. This requirement is met by the trigonometric function

$$g_n(z) = \sin \frac{\pi z}{h} \tag{8-26}$$

which has zeros at $z = jh; j = 0, \pm 1, \pm 2, \pm \ldots$. Thus the zeros of $g(z)$

have the desired property in that they form a set of equidistant points which lie on a straight line with the central sample point located at the origin.

Replace $g_n(z)$ by $g(z)$ in Eq. (8-24) to obtain the desired generalized form

$$P = \sin\frac{\pi z}{h} \sum_{j=-\infty}^{\infty} (-1)^j \frac{x_j}{z - z_j}. \tag{8-27}$$

This series is known as the *cardinal series*.

For convenience, introduce the function

$$A(y) = \max_{-\infty < z < \infty} |x(ze^{i\phi})|, \tag{8-28}$$

for any entire function x and constant ϕ; whenever the maximum value exists.

Jagerman and Fogel proved the following theorem.

Theorem 8.1: The entire function $x(z)$ can be represented as

$$x(z) = \sum_{j=-\infty}^{\infty} x_j \frac{\sin \pi(z - jh)/h}{\pi(z - jh)/h}, \tag{8-29}$$

where the cardinal series is convergent in any domain of the z-plane, $x_j = x(jh)$, $h = |h|e^{i\phi}$, if there exists a constant K such that

$$A(y) \exp(-\pi|y|/|h|) \leq \frac{K}{|y|}, \qquad \text{for} \quad |y| \to \infty. \tag{8-30}$$

One should note the obvious similarity between Eq. (8-29) and Eq. (8-15). The form of the cardinal series in Eq. (8-29) is that of a convolution with kernel $\frac{\sin \pi z/h}{\pi z/h}$. For physical applications of the theorem one restricts z to the real axis and requires that $h \geq 0$. Now investigate the frequency spectrum of this kernel by evaluating its Fourier transform.

$$\begin{aligned} \mathfrak{F}\left\{\frac{\sin \pi x/h}{\pi x/h}\right\} &= \int_{-\infty}^{\infty} \frac{\sin \pi x/h}{\pi x/h} e^{-i\omega x}\, dx \\ &= h, \qquad |\omega| < \pi/h \\ &= 0, \qquad |\omega| > \pi/h. \end{aligned} \tag{8-31}$$

This is recognized as the frequency spectrum characteristic of a low pass filter. However, because the kernel is employed as a convolution sum rather than in an integral, the interpretation of the low pass filter analogy requires a modified interpretation.

Assume that we have a sequence of narrow pulses occurring periodically with period $1/h$, having width τ and amplitude x_j. If this time series is passed through a low pass filter the output is closely approximated by the expression

$$y = \tau \sum_{j=-\infty}^{\infty} x_j \frac{\sin \pi(z - jh)/h}{\pi(z - jh)/h}; \tag{8-32}$$

the approximation improves as τ decreases. Thus if $x(z)$ satisfies the hypotheses of Theorem 8.1, the output of the filter closely approximates $\tau x(z)$.

There have been many other generalizations of the sampling theorem from the form stated in Eq. (8-15), [89, 90, 91, 92]. One of the interesting variations is based upon properties of the solutions of self-adjoint differential equations.

The representation of Eq. (8-15) is based upon the ability to express $x(t)$ in the form of a truncated Fourier integral representation, Eq. (8-11), i.e.,

$$x\,(t) = \int_{-\lambda}^{\lambda} G(f) \exp\,(2\pi i f t)\, df. \tag{8-33}$$

Kramer, [90], inquired into the possibility of using sampled values to reconstruct $x(t)$ when the exponential kernel is replaced by some other kernel and the domain $(\lambda, -\lambda)$ is replaced by some other interval, I. Kramer posed the general problem: If

$$x(t) = \int_I k(t, f)G(f)\, dx, \tag{8-34}$$

what must be the conditions imposed upon the kernel to permit the representation

$$x(t) = \Sigma f(t_n)S_n(t), \tag{8-35}$$

where $\{t_n\}$ are a set of sampling points and $\{S_n(t)\}$ a corresponding set of functions?

Define the differential operator $L(u)$ and its adjoint $L^+(u)$ by the expressions

$$L(u) = p_0 D_u^n + p_1 D_u^{n-1} + \ldots + p_n \tag{8-36}$$

$$L^+(u) = (-1)^n D^n(p_0^* u) + (-1)^{n-1} D^{n-1}(p_1^* u) + \ldots + p_n^*, \tag{8-37}$$

where $D^k = d^k/dx^k$ and $p_n(x)$ is a complex valued function on the interval I having $n - k$ derivatives; $|p_0(x)| \neq 0$. The asterisk denotes the complex conjugate.

Kramer proved the following theorem.

Theorem 8.2: Let $L(u) = tu$, $B_1(u) = B_2(u) = \ldots = B_n(u) = 0$, be a self-adjoint boundary value problem for an n'th order differential expression L on the finite interval (a, b). Suppose there exists a solution $u(t, f)$ of the differential equation $L(u) = tu$ such that the set of zeros E_i of $B_i\,[u(t, f)]$ is independent of i. Then for all functions having the representation

$$x(t) = \int_a^b u(t, f)G(f)\, df, \tag{8-38}$$

$$G(f) \in L_2(a, b)$$

there is the representation

(8-39) $$x(t) = \lim_{N\to\infty} \sum_{|k|\leq N} x(t_k)S_k(t),$$

where

(8-40) $$S_k(t) = \frac{\int_I u(t, f)u^*(t_k, f)\, df}{\int_I |u(t_k, f)|^2\, df}.$$

A simple example illustrates that Kramer's theorem reduces to the classical representation of Eq. (8-15).

Let

(8-41) $$L(u) = \frac{i}{2\pi}\frac{du}{df}$$

and

(8-42) $$B_1(u) = u(a) - u(b) = u(-\lambda) - u(\lambda).$$

The general solution of the differential equation

(8-43) $$L(u) = tu$$

for this case is:

(8-44) $$-\frac{i}{2\pi}\frac{du}{df} = tu$$

or

$$u(t, f) = A \exp{(2\pi i f t)}.$$

The eigenvalues are

(8-45) $$t_n = \frac{n}{b - a} = \frac{n}{2\lambda}; \qquad n = 0, \pm 1, \pm 2, \ldots;$$

and the corresponding eigenfunctions are

(8-46) $$u(t_n, f) = \exp\left(\frac{2\pi i n f}{2\lambda}\right).$$

Therefore from Eq. (8-40), we obtain

(8-47) $$S_n(t) = \frac{\exp\left[2\pi i \left(t - \frac{n}{2\lambda}\right)\right] - \exp\left[-2\pi i \lambda \left(t - \frac{n}{2\lambda}\right)\right]}{2\lambda \cdot 2\pi i \left(t - \frac{n}{2\lambda}\right)}$$

$$= \frac{\sin 2\pi\lambda \left(t - \frac{n}{2\lambda}\right)}{2\pi\lambda\left(t - \frac{n}{2\lambda}\right)}.$$

Combining Eq. (8-47) and Eq. (8-39) produces the expected result of Eq. (8-15).

Although various forms of the sampling theorem have been known for years, they have often been applied to random processes in a formal fashion without inquiring if the resulting representations have any validity. Sampling theorems can, of course, be formulated for representing random processes and one such theorem has been chosen to illustrate the care that must be exercised when trying to extend theorems and statements from real function theory to random processes; [91, 92].

Balakrishran proved the following theorem;

Theorem 8.3: Let $x(t)$, $-\infty < t < \infty$, be a real or complex valued wide sense stationary process whose spectral density vanishes outside the interval $(-2\pi\omega, 2\pi\omega)$. Then $x(t)$ can be represented by the series

$$x(t) = \text{l.i.m.} \sum_{n=-\infty}^{\infty} x\left(\frac{n}{2\omega}\right) \frac{\sin \pi(2\omega t - n)}{\pi(2\omega t - n)}. \tag{8-48}$$

The representation is in the mean limit sense, or

$$\lim_{N\to\infty} E\left\{\left[\left|x(t) - \sum_{n=-N}^{n} x\left(\frac{n}{2\omega}\right) \frac{\sin \pi(2\omega t - n)}{\pi(2\omega t - n)}\right|\right]^2\right\} = 0. \tag{8-49}$$

Let $G(f)$ be the spectral density function of the process $x(t)$, then the covariance function can be written as

$$R(\tau - \sigma) = \int_{-\omega}^{\omega} G(f) \exp\left[2\pi i f(\tau - \sigma)\right] df. \tag{8-50}$$

Write the exponential kernel as a Fourier series for the interval $(-\omega, \omega)$;

$$\exp(2\pi i f t) = \sum_{n=-\infty}^{\infty} a_n \exp(i n \pi f/\omega), \tag{8-51}$$

where the coefficients are

$$a_n = \frac{1}{2\lambda} \int_{-\omega}^{\omega} \exp(2\pi i f t) \exp(-i\pi f/\omega)\, df \tag{8-52}$$

$$= \frac{\sin \pi(2\omega t - n)}{\pi(2\omega t - n)}.$$

Since $\exp(i2\pi f t)$ is absolutely continuous in the interval $(-\omega, \omega)$, the series representation converges and is bounded in the open interval. Therefore the conditions are satisfied for applying the Lesbesgue convergence theorem [93, p. 345] to Eq. (8-50) where the kernel has been replaced by its series representation. Hence

$$R(\tau - \sigma) = \lim_{N\to\infty} \int_{-\omega}^{\omega} \sum_{n=-N}^{N} a_n \exp(i\pi n f/\omega) \exp(-2\pi i f \sigma) G(f)\, df. \tag{8-53}$$

Interchanging the order of summation and integration,

$$R\left(\frac{n}{2\omega} - \sigma\right) = \int_{-\omega}^{\omega} G(f) \exp(i\pi n f/\omega) \exp(-2\pi i f \sigma)\, df. \tag{8-54}$$

Thus, from Eqs. (8-50) and (8-54),

$$R(\tau - \sigma) = \sum_{n=-\infty}^{\infty} R\left(\frac{n}{2\omega} - \sigma\right) \frac{\sin \pi(2\omega\tau - n)}{(2\omega\tau - n)}. \tag{8-55}$$

Let $\hat{x}(t)$ be the best linear estimate of the process $x(t)$ in the mean square sense based upon the sampled values $\left\{x\left(\frac{n}{2\omega}\right)\right\}$. Then we can write

$$\hat{x}(t) = \text{l.i.m.} \sum_{n=-\infty}^{\infty} x\left(\frac{n}{2\omega}\right) a_n(t). \tag{8-56}$$

The theorem follows by showing that

$$Q = E\{|x(t) - \hat{x}(t)|^2\} = 0. \tag{8-57}$$

Write out the expected value, using the fact that $\hat{x}(t)$ is the best estimate in the mean square sense,

$$\begin{aligned} Q &= E\{[x(t) - \hat{x}(t)][x^*(t) - \hat{x}^*(t)]\} \\ &= E\{x(t)x^*(t)\} + E\{\hat{x}(t)\hat{x}^*(t)\} - E\{x(t)\hat{x}^*(t)\} - E\{\hat{x}(t)x^*(t)\} \\ &= R(0) + R(0) - 2E\{\hat{x}(t)x^*(t)\} \\ &= 2R(0) - 2E\left\{\text{l.i.m.} \sum_{n=-\infty}^{\infty} x\left(\frac{n}{2\omega}\right) x^*(t)a_n(t)\right\} \\ &= 2R(0) - 2\sum_{n=-\infty}^{\infty} R\left(\frac{n}{2\omega} - t\right) \frac{\sin \pi(2\omega t - n)}{\pi(2\omega t - n)} \\ &= 2[R(0) - 2R(t - t)]. \end{aligned} \tag{8-58}$$

This establishes the theorem.

8.4 SIGNAL QUANTIZING

Modern communication systems often require that a time series be converted into digital numbers for transmission and reconstructed at the receiver. The sampled signals are often quantized before transmission. That is, all signal amplitudes lying within a given range are arbitrarily assigned the same amplitude. The difference between the original sample amplitude and the corresponding quantized amplitude is called the quantizing error. A typical quantizing characteristic is shown in Figure 8-1. To accommodate a finite channel transmission rate, the quantizer sorts the original process into a finite number of amplitudes, N. The quantizer is characterized by specifying the amplitude limits x_i corresponding to each step of the output level y_i. Two cases are of general interest. The first corresponds to equal quantized steps and the second uses unequal steps in an effort to reduce the quantizing error.

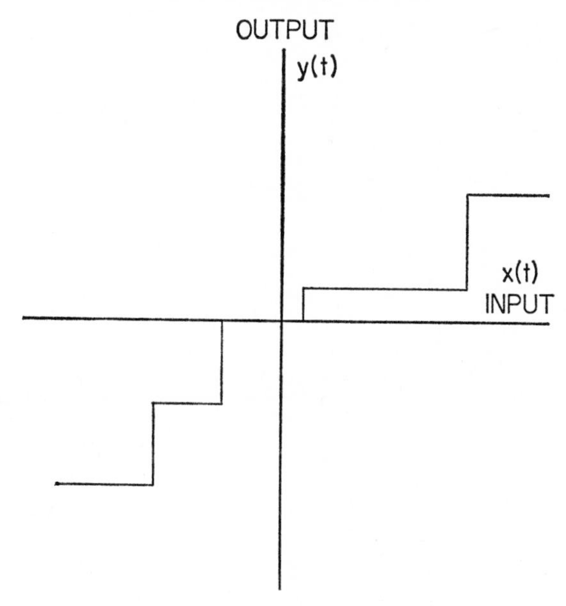

Figure 8-1. Quantizing Characteristic

8.4.1 EQUAL STEPS

For equal quantized steps of amplitude m, the output signal can be written as

(8-59) $$y_i = mx_0; \qquad m = 0, \pm 1, \pm 2, \pm \ldots$$

and

(8-60) $$\frac{2m-1}{2} x_0 < x < \frac{2m+1}{2} x_0.$$

By definition, the quantizing error is

(8-61) $$\begin{aligned} z(t_i) &= x(t_i) - y(t_i) \\ &= x_i - y_i \\ &= x_i - mx_0. \end{aligned}$$

The covariance of the quantizing error is

(8-62) $$\begin{aligned} \psi(\tau) &= E\{z(t)z(t+\tau)\} \\ &= E\{(x_i - mx_0)(x_j - nx_0)\}. \end{aligned}$$

Assume that $x_i = x_1$ and $x_j = x_2$ are Gaussian distributed correlated variables having the joint frequency function

(8-63) $$f(x_1, x_2) = \frac{1}{2\pi\sqrt{\sigma^4 - R_\tau^2}} \exp\left[-\frac{\sigma^2(x_1^2 + x_2^2) - 2R_\tau x_1 x_2}{2(\sigma^4 - R_\tau^2)}\right].$$

Make the change of variables

$$x_1 - mx_0 = x_0u/2 \tag{8-64}$$
$$x_2 - nx_0 = x_0v/2$$
$$k = x_0^2/\sigma^2$$
$$\rho = R_\tau/\sigma^2$$
$$G(\rho) = \psi(\tau)/\sigma^2.$$

in Eq. (8-63). Using the result in Eq. (8-62) yields

$$G(\rho) = \frac{k^2}{32\pi(1-\rho^2)^{1/2}} \int_{-1}^{1}\int_{-1}^{1} uvH(u, v) \exp\left[-\frac{k(u^2+v^2-2\rho uv)}{8(1-\rho^2)}\right] du\, dv, \tag{8-65}$$

where

$$H(u, v) = \sum_{m,n=-\infty}^{\infty} \exp\left\{\frac{-k[m^2 + m(u-\rho v) + n^2 + n(v - \rho u) - 2\rho mn]}{2(1-\rho^2)}\right\}. \tag{8-66}$$

Bennett [94], has shown that Eq. (8-65) can be reduced to the form

$$G(\rho) = \frac{k}{\pi^2}\sum_{m=1}^{\infty}\frac{1}{n^2}\exp\left(-\frac{4n^2\pi^2}{k}\right)\sinh\frac{4n^2\pi^2\rho}{k} \tag{8-67}$$
$$+ \frac{k}{\pi^2}\sum_{m,n=1}^{\infty}(m \neq n)\frac{1}{(m^2-n^2)}\exp\left[-\frac{4(m^2+n^2)\pi^2}{k}\right]\sinh\frac{4(m^2-n^2)\pi^2\rho}{k}$$
$$- \frac{k}{\pi^2}\sum_{m,n=1}^{\infty}(m \neq n)\left[\left(m-\frac{1}{2}\right)^2 - \left(n - \frac{1}{2}\right)^2\right]^{-1} \exp\left\{\frac{-4[(m-\frac{1}{2})^2 + (n-\frac{1}{2})^2]\pi^2}{k}\right\}$$
$$\cdot \sinh\left\{\frac{4[(m-\frac{1}{2})^2 - (n-\frac{1}{2})^2]\pi^2\rho}{k}\right\}.$$

Even for a relatively few steps $1/k$ is sufficiently small to permit the approximation

$$G(\rho) \approx \frac{k}{\pi^2}\sum_{n=1}^{\infty}\frac{1}{n^2}\exp\left[\frac{-4n^2\pi^2(1-\rho)}{k}\right]. \tag{8-68}$$

The point spectral density of the quantization errors is obtained from the transform of $G(\rho)$, or

$$W(f) = 4\sigma^2\int_0^{\infty} G(\rho)\cos 2\pi f\tau\, d\tau. \tag{8-69}$$

Suppose, for example, that the input process has a flat spectrum from $f = 0$ to $f = f_0$ and no energy outside this region. This corresponds to

(8-70) $$\rho = \frac{1}{f_0}\int_0^{f_0} \cos 2\pi f\tau\, df = \frac{\sin 2\pi f_0\tau}{2\pi f_0\tau}.$$

Let $\gamma = f/f_0$, then

(8-71) $$W(\gamma) = \frac{f_0 W(f)}{\sigma^2} = \frac{2}{\pi}\int_0^{\infty} G\left(\frac{\sin z}{z}\right) \cos \gamma z\, dz.$$

Insert Eq. (8-68) in Eq. (8-71);

(8-72) $$W(\gamma) = \frac{k}{\pi^3}\sum_{n=1}^{\infty}\frac{1}{n^2}\int_0^{\infty} \exp\left[\frac{-4n^2\pi^2}{k}\left(1 - \frac{\sin z}{z}\right)\right] \cos \gamma z\, dz.$$

The integral is negligible except for values of z in the neighborhood of zero. In this neighborhood, we can approximate $\frac{1}{z}\sin z$ by the first two terms in its series representation to obtain

(8-73) $$W(\gamma) = \frac{k}{\pi^3}\sum_{n=1}^{\infty}\frac{1}{n^2}\int_0^{\infty} \exp\left(\frac{-2n^2\pi^2 z^2}{3k}\right) \cos \gamma z\, dz$$

$$= \frac{k}{2\pi^3}\sqrt{\frac{3k}{2\pi}}\sum_{n=1}^{\infty}\frac{1}{n^3}\exp\left(\frac{-3k\gamma^2}{8n^2\pi^2}\right).$$

8.4.2 UNEQUAL STEPS

Unequal steps in the quantizer are often employed to reduce the signal distortion that is found after reconstructing a process from the quantized signals. One method of defining distortion, D, is to choose

(8-74) $$D = E\{g(z)\}$$
$$= E\{g(x_i - y_i)\},$$

where z is the quantization error and g is some suitable differential function. We can write Eq. (8-74) in the form

(8-75) $$D = \sum_{i=1}^{N}\int_{x_i}^{x_{i+1}} g(x - y_i)f(x)\, dx,$$

where $f(x)$ is the frequency function of the original process $x(t)$ and y_i is the output corresponding to an input signal in the range (x_i, x_{i+1}).

The necessary conditions for minimizing D for a fixed number of steps N are found by differentiating Eq. (8-75). These conditions are:

(8-76) $$\frac{\partial D}{\partial x_j} = 0 = g(x_j - y_{j-1})f(x_j) - g(x_j - y_j)f(x_j)$$

or

$$g(x_j - y_{j-1}) = g(x_j - y_j); \quad j = 1, 2, \ldots, N; \quad f(x_j) \neq 0,$$

(8-77) $$\frac{\partial D}{\partial y_j} = -\int_{x_i}^{x_{j+1}} g'(x - y_j)f(x)\, dx = 0; \quad j = 1, 2, \ldots, N.$$

For arbitrary functions g, these equations are difficult to solve. Even for particular choices the solutions are not easy to find. Max [95], obtained numerical solutions for the function $g(x) = x^2$. A table of numerical values appears in his paper.

The converse problem is often of greater practical importance. Given $g(x)$, determine the size of the quantizing interval which yields the minimum distortion for a given number of steps, N. For an even number of output levels, $2N$,

$$D = 2 \sum_{i=1}^{N-1} \int_{(i-1)m}^{im} g\left[x - \left(\frac{2i-1}{2}\right)m\right] f(x)\,dx + 2 \int_{(N-1)m}^{\infty} g\left[x - \left(\frac{2N-1}{2}\right)m\right] f(x)\,dx. \tag{8-78}$$

The minimum is obtained by differentiating this expression with respect to m, the common length of the intervals, and equating the result to zero;

$$\frac{\partial D}{\partial m} = -\sum_{i=1}^{N-1} (2i-1) \int_{(i-1)m}^{im} g'\left[x - \left(\frac{2i-1}{2}\right)m\right] f(x)\,dx - (2N-1) \int_{(N-1)m}^{\infty} g'\left[x - \left(\frac{2N-1}{2}\right)m\right] f(x)\,dx = 0. \tag{8-79}$$

Numerical results have been obtained for the case $g(x) = x^2$, when x is a Gaussian process, [95].

Appendix NOTES ON HYPERGEOMETRIC FUNCTIONS

A collection of notes on the hypergeometric function are presented for reference use. These relations occur very frequently in the solution of problems involving nonlinear problems. Often integrations are accomplished by expanding a transcendental function and termwise integrating the resulting series. The solution can be reduced frequently to a recognizable form by first placing the series in the form of a hypergeometric function and then applying transformations to get the form into one that is recognizable. This appendix contains some of the most frequently used relations required to carry out this procedure.

FACTORIAL FUNCTION

The factorial function $(a)_n$ may be defined by the relations

$$(1)\qquad \begin{aligned} (a)_n &= a(a+1)(a+2)\dots(a+n-1); \qquad n > 0, \qquad n \text{ an integer} \\ (a)_0 &= 1. \end{aligned}$$

It is convenient to have a table of certain relations involving the factorial function. These are tabulated without proof.

$$(2)\qquad (a)_n = \frac{\Gamma(a+n)}{\Gamma(a)}; \qquad a \neq 0,\ -1,\ -2.$$

$$(3)\qquad (a)_{n+1} = (a)_n(a+n).$$

$$(4)\qquad (a+1)_{n-1} = \frac{(a)_n}{a}.$$

$$(a+1)_n = \frac{(a)_n(a+n)}{a}. \tag{5}$$

$$(a-1)_n = \frac{(a)_n(a-1)}{a+n-1}. \tag{6}$$

$$\left(\frac{1}{2}\right)_n = \frac{(2n)!}{2^{2n}n!}. \tag{7}$$

$$\frac{k!}{(k-s)!} = (-1)^s(-k)_s. \tag{8}$$

$$(-m)_m = (-1)^m m!. \tag{9}$$

$$(1-n)_k = \frac{(-1)^k(n-1)!}{(n-k-1)!}. \tag{10}$$

$$(a)_{n-k} = \frac{(a)_n}{(-1)^k(1-a-n)_k}. \tag{11}$$

$$(a)_{n+k} = (a)_n(a+n)_k. \tag{12}$$

$$(2k+1)_n = \frac{(2k+n)!}{(2k)!}. \tag{13}$$

$$\frac{(n+k)!}{(n-k)!} = (-1)^k(-n)_k(n+1)_k. \tag{14}$$

$$(a)_{2n} = 2^{2n}\left(\frac{a}{2}\right)_n\left(\frac{a+1}{2}\right)_n. \tag{15}$$

$$(a)_{nk} = (k)^{nk}\left(\frac{a}{k}\right)_n\left(\frac{a+1}{k}\right)_n\cdots\left(\frac{a+k-1}{k}\right)_n. \tag{16}$$

HYPERGEOMETRIC FUNCTION

The ordinary hypergeometric function is defined by the series

$$F(a, b; c; z) = \sum_{k=0}^{\infty} \frac{(a)_k(b)_k}{(c)_k}\frac{z^k}{k!}. \tag{17}$$

The generalized hypergeometric function is defined by an obvious extension of Eq. (17). Thus the generalized hypergeometric function with p numerator parameters and q denominator parameters is written as

$$\begin{aligned} {}_pF_q &= F(a_1, a_2, \ldots, a_p; b_1, b_2, \ldots, b_q; z) \\ &= \sum_{k=0}^{\infty} \frac{(a_1)_k(a_2)_k \ldots (a_p)_k}{(b_1)_k(b_2)_k \ldots (b_q)_k}\frac{z^k}{k!}. \end{aligned} \tag{18}$$

To conserve space, Eq. (18) is sometimes written in the form

$${}_pF_q = {}_pF_q\left[\begin{matrix} a_1, a_2, \ldots, a_p; \\ b_1, b_2, \ldots, b_q; \end{matrix}\; z\right]. \tag{19}$$

If n is zero or a positive integer, Eq. (8) indicates that

$$(-n)_k = \frac{(-1)^k n!}{(n-k)!}. \tag{20}$$

This implies that for $k > 0$, $(-n)_k = 0$. Therefore it is generally necessary to restrict the denominator parameter, b, in $F(a, b; c; z)$ not to be a non-positive integer. If the denominator is a negative integer then at least one of the numerator parameters must be a non-positive integer. The hypergeometric series then will be well-defined, provided that the zero in the numerator enters the series to terminate it before the zero appears in the denominator.

For example, notice that the following series terminates for a non-positive integer in a numerator parameter.

$$F(-2, 1; 6; z) = \sum_{k=0}^{\infty} \frac{(-2)_k(1)_k}{(6)_k} \frac{z^k}{k!} = 1 + \frac{(-2)(1)}{6} \frac{z}{1!} + \frac{(-2)(-1)(1)(2)}{6 \cdot 5} \frac{z^2}{2!} + \frac{(-2)(-1)(0)1 \cdot 2 \cdot 3}{6 \cdot 5 \cdot 4} \frac{z^3}{3} = 1 - \tfrac{1}{3}z + \tfrac{1}{15}z^2. \tag{21}$$

If n and m are positive integers, then $b = -m$ is permissible if $a = -n$ and $n < m$. Consider

$$F(-1, 2; -2; z) = \sum_{k=0}^{\infty} \frac{(-1)_k(2)_k}{(-2)_k} \frac{z^k}{k!} = 1 + \frac{(-1)(2)}{-2} \frac{z}{1!} + \frac{(-1)(0)2 \cdot 3}{(-2)(-1)} \frac{z^2}{2!} = 1 - z. \tag{22}$$

A SELECTED LIST OF HYPERGEOMETRIC FUNCTIONS

The absence of parameters in either the numerator or denominator is indicated by a dash. Some of the functions may be listed in an unfamiliar form. The factorial function relations can be used to reduce these series to more familiar terms. For example consider

$$(1 + z)^n = F(-n; -; -z).$$

From Eq. (18)

$$(1 + z)^n = \sum_{k=0}^{\infty} (-n)_k \frac{(z)^k}{k!}.$$

Insert Eq. (8),

$$(1 + z)^n = \sum_{k=0}^{\infty} \frac{(-1)^k n!}{(n-k)!} \frac{(-1)^k z^k}{k!} = \sum_{k=0}^{\infty} \frac{n!}{k!(n-k)!} z^k.$$

(23) *Exponential Function*

$$e^z = F(-;-;z).$$

(24) *Binomial Expansion*

$$(1+z)^n = F(-n;-;-z); \qquad n \text{ need not be integral.}$$

(25) *Bessel Function*

$$J_n(z) = \frac{(z/2)^n}{\Gamma(n+1)} F(-;n+1;-z^2/4); \qquad n \text{ need not be integral.}$$

(26) *Modified Bessel Function*

$$I_n(z) = \frac{(z/2)^n}{\Gamma(n+1)} F(-;n+1;z^2/4).$$

(27) *Incomplete Gamma Function*

$$\gamma(\alpha, x) = \int_0^x e^{-t} t^{\alpha-1}\, dt,$$

$$\gamma(\alpha, x) = \alpha^{-1} x^\alpha F(\alpha; \alpha+1; -x).$$

(28) *Error Function*

$$\text{Erf}\,(x) = \int_0^x e^{-t^2}\, dt,$$

$$\text{Erf}\,(x) = xF(\tfrac{1}{2}; \tfrac{3}{2}; -x^2).$$

(29) *Laguerre Polynomials*

$$L_n(x) = F(-n;1;x); \qquad n \text{ integral.}$$

(30) *Sonine Polynomials—Generalized Laguerre Polynomials*

$$L_n^{(\alpha)}(x) = \frac{(\alpha+1)_n}{n!} F(-n;\alpha+1;x); \qquad n \text{ integral.}$$

(31) *Hermite Polynomials—even index*

$$H_{2n}(x) = (-1)^n 2^{2n} (\tfrac{1}{2})_n F(-n; \tfrac{1}{2}; x^2); \qquad n \text{ integral.}$$

(32) *Hermite Polynomials—odd index*

$$H_{2n+1}(x) = (-1)^n 2^{2n+1} (\tfrac{3}{2})_n x F(-n; \tfrac{3}{2}; x^2); \qquad n \text{ integral.}$$

(33) *One of Whittaker's Functions*

$$M_{k,m}(z) = z^{1/2+m} e^{-z/2} F(m-k+\tfrac{1}{2}; 2m+1; z).$$

(34) *Jacobi Polynomials*

$$P_n^{(\alpha,\beta)}(x) = \frac{(\alpha+1)_n}{n!}$$

$$F(-n, \alpha+\beta+n+1; \alpha+1; (1-x)/2), \qquad n \text{ integral.}$$

(35) *Ultraspherical Polynomials*

$$P_n^{(\alpha,\alpha)}(x) = \frac{(\alpha+1)_n}{n!} F(-n, n+2\alpha+1; \alpha+1; (1-x)/2), \qquad n \text{ integral.}$$

(36) *Legendre Polynomials*

$$P_n(x) = F(-n, n+1; 1; (1-x)/2), \qquad n \text{ integral.}$$

(37) ln (*1* + x)

$$\ln(1+x) = xF(1, 1; 2; -x).$$

(38) Arcsin x

$$\arcsin x = xF(\tfrac{1}{2}, \tfrac{1}{2}; \tfrac{3}{2}; x^2).$$

(39) Arctan x

$$\arctan x = xF(\tfrac{1}{2}, 1; \tfrac{3}{2}; -x^{-2}).$$

(40) *Complete Elliptic Integral—first kind*

$$K = \int_0^{\pi/2} (1 - \lambda^2 \sin^2\theta)^{-1/2}\, d\theta$$

$$K = \frac{\pi}{2} F(\tfrac{1}{2}, \tfrac{1}{2}; 1; \lambda^2).$$

(41) *Complete Elliptic Integral—second kind*

$$E = \int_0^{\pi/2} (1 - \lambda^2 \sin^2\theta)^{1/2}\, d\theta$$

$$E = \frac{\pi}{2} F(\tfrac{1}{2}, -\tfrac{1}{2}; 1; \lambda^2).$$

(42) *Gottlieb Polynomials*

(Amer. Journal of Math., 60, 1938, 453–458)

$$l_n(x; \lambda) = e^{-n\lambda} F(-n, -x; 1; 1 - e^{\lambda}); \qquad n \text{ integral.}$$

(43) *Struve's Function*

$$H_\gamma(z) = \frac{(z/2)^{\gamma+1}}{\Gamma(\frac{3}{2})\Gamma(\gamma+\frac{3}{2})} F(1; \tfrac{3}{2}, \gamma+\tfrac{3}{2}; -z^2/4).$$

EVALUATION OF A CLASS OF DEFINITE INTEGRALS

A large number of definite integrals that often arise during the solution of applied problems are special cases of the following integral:

$$(44) \qquad A = \int_0^t x^{a-1}(t-x)^{b-1} {}_pF_q\left[\begin{matrix}\alpha_1, \alpha_2, \ldots, \alpha_p; \\ \beta_1, \beta_2, \ldots, \beta_q;\end{matrix} \rho x^k(t-x)^m\right] dx,$$

where the parameters are subject to the conditions:

(i) Re $(a) > 0$
(ii) Re $(b) > 0$
(iii) k and m are non-negative integers, not both zero.
(iv) $p \leq q + 1$; unless some α is a nonpositive integer, in which case p may be any positive integer.

Make the change of variable $x = tv$ and Eq. (44) becomes

(45)

$$A = t^{a+b-1} \int_0^1 v^{a-1}(1-v)^{b-1} {}_pF_q\left[\begin{matrix}\alpha_1, \ldots, \alpha_p; \\ \beta_1, \ldots, \beta_q;\end{matrix} \rho t^{k+m}v^k(1-v)^m\right] dv$$

$$= t^{a+b-1} \int_0^1 \sum_{n=0}^{\infty} \frac{\prod_{i=1}^{p} (\alpha_i)_n}{\prod_{j=1}^{\beta} (\beta_j)_n} \frac{t^{n(k+m)}\rho^n v^{a-1+kn}(1-v)^{b-1+mn}}{n!} dv.$$

After termwise integration,

$$(46) \qquad A = t^{a+b-1} \sum_{n=0}^{\infty} \frac{\prod_{i=1}^{p} (\alpha_i)_n}{\prod_{k=1}^{q} (\beta_j)_n} \frac{\rho^n t^{n(k+m)} B(a+kn, b+mn)}{n!},$$

where $B(x, y)$ is the usual Beta function. Express this function in terms of Gamma functions by the relation

$$(47) \qquad B(a+kn, b+mn) = \frac{\Gamma(a+kn)\Gamma(b+mn)}{\Gamma(a+b+kn+mn)}.$$

Apply Eq. (2) to Eq. (47);

$$(48) \qquad B(a+kn, b+mn) = \frac{\Gamma(a)\Gamma(b)}{\Gamma(a+b)} \cdot \frac{(a)_{kn}(b)_{mn}}{(a+b)_{(k+m)n}}.$$

Now use Eq. (16) in Eq. (48);

$$(49) \qquad B(a+kn, b+mn)$$

$$= \frac{B(a, b)k^{kn}m^{mn} \left(\frac{a}{k}\right)_n \cdots \left(\frac{a+k-1}{k}\right)_m \cdot \left(\frac{b}{m}\right) \cdots \left(\frac{b+m-1}{m}\right)_n}{(k+m)^{(k+m)n} \left(\frac{a+b}{k+m}\right)_n \left(\frac{a+b+1}{k+m}\right)_n \cdots \left(\frac{a+b+k+m-1}{k+m}\right)_n}.$$

Combine Eq. (49) with Eq. (46) to obtain

$$A = B(a, b)t^{a+b-1} \sum_{n=0}^{\infty} \frac{\left[\prod_{i=1}^{p} (\alpha_i)_n\right]}{\left[\prod_{j=1}^{q} (\beta_j)_n\right]} \frac{(\rho t^{k+m})^n k^{kn} m^{mn} \left[\prod_{s=1}^{k} \left(\frac{a+s-1}{k}\right)\right]\left[\prod_{r=1}^{m}\left(\frac{b+r-1}{m}\right)_n\right]}{n!(k+m)^{(k+m)n}\left[\prod_{\sigma=1}^{k+m}\left(\frac{a+b+\sigma-1}{k+m}\right)_n\right]}. \tag{50}$$

Therefore, the final result is

$$\int_0^t x^{a-1}(t-x)^{b-1}\, {}_pF_q\left[\begin{matrix}\alpha_1, \ldots, \alpha_p; \\ \beta_1, \ldots, \beta_q;\end{matrix}\ \rho x^k (t-x)^m\right] dx \tag{73-60}$$

$$= B(a, b)t^{a+b-1}\ {}_{p+k+m}F_{q+k+m}$$

$$\left[\begin{matrix}\alpha_1, \ldots, \alpha_p, \frac{a}{k}, \ldots, \frac{a+k-1}{k}, \frac{b}{m}, \ldots, \frac{b+m-1}{m}; \\ \beta_1, \ldots, \beta_q, \frac{a+b}{k+m}, \ldots, \frac{a+b+k+m-1}{k+m};\end{matrix}\ \frac{k^k m^m \rho t^{k+m}}{(k+m)^{(k+m)}}\right].$$

As an example consider the integral

$$N = \int_0^t J_0[\sqrt{x(t-x)}]\, dx. \tag{51}$$

From Eq. (24),

$$N = \int_0^t {}_pF_q\left(-; 1; -\frac{x(t-x)}{4}\right) dx. \tag{52}$$

Now apply Eq. (50) with

$p = 0$	$a = 1$	$\rho = -\frac{1}{4}$	$m = 1$
$q = 1$	$b = 1$	$k = 1$	$\beta_1 = 1.$

Thus

$$N = B(1, 1)t\ {}_2F_3\left(1, 1; \tfrac{2}{2}, \tfrac{3}{2}; \frac{-\frac{1}{4}t^2}{2^2}\right) = tF\left(-; \tfrac{3}{2}; -\frac{t^2}{16}\right). \tag{53}$$

From the list of hypergeometric functions, this is recognized as Eq. (24),

$$N = J_{1/2}\left(\frac{t}{2}\right) \cdot \frac{1}{\Gamma(\frac{3}{2})} = 2 \sin \frac{t}{2}. \tag{54}$$

References

1. Titchmarsh, E. C., *Introduction to the Theory of Fourier Integrals.* New York: Oxford University Press, 1937.
2. Dugundji, J., "Envelopes and Pre-Envelopes of Real Waveforms," *I.R.E. Trans. PGIT*, **IT-4,** No. 1 (March 1958), 53.
3. Gabor, D., "Theory of Communication," *J.I.E.E.*, **93,** Part 3 (1946), 429.
4. Ville, J. A., "Théorie et Application de la Notion de Signal Analytique," *Cables et Transmissions.* **2** (1948), 61–74.
5. Zakai, M., "Second-Order Properties of the Pre-Envelope and Envelope Processes," *I.R.E. Trans. PGIT*, **IT-6,** No. 5 (December 1960), 556.
6. Brown, W. M., "Some Results on Noise Through Circuits," *I.R.E. Trans. PGIT*, **CT-6** (May 1959), 217.
7. Karr, P. R., "An Inequality Concerning the Envelope of a Correlation Function," *I.R.E. Trans. PGIT*, **IT-5,** No. 1 (March 1959), 33.
8. Hoffman, W. C., "The Joint Distribution of n Successive Outputs of a Linear Detector," *Journal of Applied Physics*, **25** (August 1954), 1006–1007.
9. Rice, S. O., "Mathematical Analysis of Random Noise," *Bell System Technical Journal*, **24** (1945).
10. Middleton, D., "The Response of Biased, Saturated Linear and Quadratic Rectifiers to Random Noise," *Journal of Applied Physics*, **17** (1946), 778–801.
11. Kraft, L. G. and Weinberg, L., "Measurements of Detector Output Spectra by Correlation Methods," *I.R.E. Proc.*, **41** (Sept. 1955), 1757–1766.
12. Deutsch, R., "Detection of Modulated Noise-Like Signals," *I.R.E. Trans. PGIT*, **3** (March 1954), 106.
13. Young, G. O. and Gold, B., "Effect of Limiting on the Information Content of Noisy Signals," *I.R.E. Convention Record*, **Part 4** (1945), 76.
14. Campbell, L. L., "Rectification of Two Signals in Random Noise," *I.R.E. Trans. PGIT*, **IT-2** (December 1956), 119.

15. Price, R., "A Useful Theorem for Nonlinear Devices Having Gaussian Inputs," *I.R.E. Trans. PGIT*, **IT-4** (June 1958), 69.

16. Cramér, H., *Mathematical Methods of Statistics.* Princeton, N. J.: Princeton University Press, 1946.

17. Bateman Manuscript Project, *Higher Transcendental Functions.* New York: McGraw-Hill Book Co., 1953.

18. Baum, R. F., "The Correlation Function of Smoothly Limited Gaussian Noise," *I.R.E. Trans. PGIT*, **IT-3** (Sept. 1957), 193–197.

19. Lawson, J. L. and Uhlenbeck, G. E., *Threshold Signals*, MIT Radiation Lab. Series **24.** New York: McGraw-Hill Book Co., 1950.

20. Middleton, D., "Some General Remarks in the Theory of Noise Through Nonlinear Devices," *Quarterly Applied Mathematics*, **5,** No. 4 (January 1948), 445–498.

21. Watson, G. N., *A Treatise on the Theory of Bessel Functions.* Cambridge University Press, 1952.

22. Jahnke, E. and Emde, F., *Tables of Functions with Formulae and Curves.* New York: Dover (reprint 1945).

23. Deutsch, R. and Hance, H. V., "A Note on Receivers for Use in Studies of Signal Statistics," *I.R.E. Convention Record*, **pt. 8** (1953) Information Theory, p. 7.

24. Blanc-La Pierre, A. and Fortet, R., *Théorie des Fonctions Aléatoires.* Paris: Masson et Cie, 1953.

25. McFadden, J. A., "The Axis-Crossing Intervals of Random Functions," *I.R.E. Trans. on Information Theory,* **17-2,** No. 4 (December 1956), 146.

26. Craig, C. C., "On the Frequency Function of *xy*," *Annals of Math. Stat.*, **7** (1936). 1–15.

27. Aroian, L. A., "The Probability Function of the Product of Two Normally Distributed Variables," *Annals of Math. Stat.*, **18** (1947), 265–271.

28. Harrington, J. V. and Rogers, T. F., "Signal-to-Noise Improvement Through Integration in a Storage Tube," *I.R.E. Proc.* (October 1950), 1197–1203.

29. Blachman, N. M., "The Output Signal-to-Noise Ratio of a Power-Law Device," *Journal of Applied Physics*, **24** (June 1953), 783–785.

30. Karhunen, K., "Über Lineare Methoden in der Wahrscheinlichkeitsrechnung,"*Ann. Acad. Sci. Fennicae Wer. A.*, I. Math. Phys., **37** (1947).

31. Lévy, P., *Processus Stochastiques et Mouvement Brownian,* Paris: Gauthier-Villars, 1948.

32. Kac, M. and Siegert, A. J. F., "An Explicit Representation of a Stationary Gaussian Process," *Annals Math. Stat.*, **18** (1947), 38.

33. Thomas, J. B. and Zadeh, L. A., "Note on an Integral Equation Occurring in the Prediction, Detection, and Analysis of Multiple Time Series," *I.R.E. Trans. PGIT*, **IT-7** (April 1961), 118.

34. Doob, J. L. *Stochastic Processes.* New York: John Wiley, 1953.

35. Courant, R. and Hilbert, D., *Methoden der Mathematischen Physik.* New York: Interscience Publishers, 1931.

36. Kac, M. and Siegert, A. J. F., "On the Theory of Noise in Radio Receivers with Square Law Detectors," *Journal of Applied Physics,* **18** (1947), 383.

37. Siegert, A. J. F., "Passage of Stationary Processes Through Linear and Non-Linear Devices," *I.R.E. Trans. PGIT*, **3** (March 1954), 4.

38. Rosenbloom, A., Heilfron, J. and Trautman, D. C., "Analysis of Linear Systems with Randomly Varying Inputs and Parameters," *I.R.E. Convention Record,* **Pt. 4** (1955), 106.

39. Emerson, R. C., "First Probability Densities for Receivers with Square Law Detectors," *Journal of Applied Physics,* **24** (1953), 1168.

40. Meyer, M. A. and Middleton, D., "On the Distributions of Signals and Noise After Rectification and Filtering," *Journal of Applied Physics,* **25** (August 1954), 1037.

41. Rice, S. O., "Filtered Thermal Noise Fluctuation of Energy as a Function of Interval Length," *Journal of the Accoustical Society of America,* **1** (April 1943), 216–227.

42. Stone, W. M., Brock, R. L. and Hammerle, K. J., "On the First Probability of Detection by a Radar Receiver System," *I.R.E. Trans. on Information Theory PGIT*, **IT-5,** No. 1 (March 1959), 9.

43. Brown, J. L., "On the Cross Correlation Between Two Noisy Channels," *I.R.E. Trans. PGIT*, **IT-6,** No. 1 (March 1960), 54.

44. Keilson, J., Mermin, N. D. and Bello, P., "A Theorem on Cross Correlation Between Noisy Channels," *I.R.E. Trans. PGIT*, **IT-5,** No. 2 (June 1959), 77.

45. Roe, G. M. and White, G. M., "Probability Density Functions for Correlators with Noisy Reference Signals," *I.R.E. Trans. PGIT*, **IT-7,** No. 1 (January 1961), 13.

46. Middleton, D., "On the Distribution of Energy in Noise-and-Signal Modulated Waves, II. Simultaneous Amplitude and Noise Modulation," *Quarterly of Applied Mathematics*, **X** (April 1952), 37–56.

47. Middleton, D., "The Spectrum of Frequency-Modulated Waves after Reception in Random Noise, I," *Quarterly of Applied Mathematics*, **VII** (July 1949), 129–174.

48. Middleton, D., "The Spectrum of Frequency-Modulated Waves After Reception in Random Noise, II," *Quarterly of Applied Mathematics*, **VIII** (April 1950), 59–80.

49. Deutsch, R., "Detection of Modulated Noise-Like Signals," *I.R.E. Trans. PGIT*, **IT-3** (March 1954), 107–122.

50. Campbell, L. L., "Rectification of Two Signals in Random Noise," *I.R.E. Trans. PGIT*, **IT-2** (December 1956), 119–124.

51. Marcum, J. I., "A Statistical Theory of Target Detection by Pulsed Radar," *I.R.E. Trans. PGIT*, **IT-6,** No. 6 (April 1960).

52. Young, G. O., "Random Function Probability Distributions After a Nonlinear Filter," *I.R.E. Wescon Convention Record*, 1958, 164.

53. Lampard, D. G., "A New Method of Determining Correlation Functions of Stationary Time Series," *I.E.E. Monograph*, **No. 4** (August 16, 1954).

54. Horton, C. W., "The Structure of the Noise Background of a Seismogram," *Geophysics*, **XX,** No. 3 (July 1955), 565–584.

55. Horton, C. W., "On the Use of Gram-Charlier Series to Represent Noise," *Journal of Applied Physics*, **27,** No. 4 (April 1956), 350–355.

56. Barrett, J. F. and Lampard, D. G., "An Expansion for Some Second Order Probability Distributions and its Application to Noise Problems," *I.R.E. Trans. PGIT*, **IT-1** (March 1955), 10–15.

57. Bussgang, J. J., "Cross Correlation Functions of Amplitude Distorted Gaussian Signals," *MIT Res. Lab. Elec. Technical Report*, **No. 216.** Cambridge, Mass., MIT, March 1952.

58. Watson, G. N., "Generating Functions for Polynomials II," *Journal of the London Mathematical Society*, **8** (1933), 194.

59. Wiener, N., "Response of a Non-Linear Device to Noise," *MIT Rad. Lab. Report*, **168** (April 1942).

60. Shikao Ikehara, "A Method of Wiener in a Non-Linear Circuit," *MIT RLE Report*, **217** (December 1951).

61. Deutsch, R., "On a Method of Wiener for Noise Through Nonlinear Devices," *I.R.E. Convention Record*, **Pt. 4** (1955), 186–192.

62. Zadeh, L. A., "On the Representation of Nonlinear Operators," *I.R.E. Wescon Convention Record*, **Pt. 2** (1957), 105–113.

63. Volterra, V., "Sopra le funzioni che dipendono da altre funzioni," *Rend. Acc., dei lincei*, **3** (1887).

64. Cameron, R. H. and Martin, W. T., "The Orthogonal Development of Nonlinear Functionals in Series of Fourier-Hermite Functionals, *Annals of Mathematics*, **48** (April 1947), 385–392.

65. Barrett, J. F., "Application of the Theory of Functionals to Communication Problems," *Engineering Laboratory Reports*, Cambridge University, 1955.

66. Grad, H., "Note on N-dimensional Hermite Polynomials," *Communications on Pure and Applied Mathematics*, **2** (December 1949), 325–330.

67. Clavier, P. A., "Construction of Probability Densities from their Moments," *I.R.E. Proc.*, **49,** No. 10 (October 1961), 1580.

68. Schwartz, L., *Théorie des Distributions.* Paris, France: Herman and Co., 1950. V. 1 and 2.

69. Kac, M., "On the Average of a Certain Wiener Functional and a Related Theorem in the Calculus of Probability," *American Mathematical Society Transactions*, **59** (1946), 401–414.

70. Cameron, R. H. and Martin, T. W., "The Wiener Measure of Hilbert Neighborhoods in the Space of Real Continuous Functions," *Journal of Mathematics and Physics*, **23** (1944), 195–209.

71. Kac, M., "On Some Connections Between Probability Theory and Differential and Integral Equations," *Proceedings of the Second Berkeley Symposium*, University of California Press (1951), 189–215.

72. Kac, M., "On the Distribution of Certain Wiener Functionals," *American Mathematical Society Transactions*, **65** (1949), 1–13.

73. Kac, M., "On Deviations Between Theoretical and Empirical Distributions," *Proceedings of the National Academy of Sciences*, **35** (1949), 252–257.

74. Rosenblatt, M., "On a Class of Markov Processes," *American Mathematical Society Transactions*, **71** (1951), 120–135.

75. Darling, D. A., and Siegert, A. J. F., "On the Distributions of Certain Functionals of Markov Processes," *The Rand Corporation Report*, **P-429** (October 1953).

76. Darling, D. A. and Siegert, A. J. F., "A Systematic Approach to a Class of Problems in the Theory of Noise and Other Random Phenomena—Part I," *I.R.E. Trans. PGIT*, **3** (March 1957), 32–37.

77. Siegert, A. J. F., "A Systematic Approach to a Class of Problems in the Theory of Noise and Other Random Phenomena—Part II, Examples," *I.R.E. Trans. PGIT*, **3** (March 1957), 38–43.

78. Siegert, A. J. F., "A Systematic Approach to a Class of Problems in the Theory of Noise and Other Random Phenomena—Part III, Examples," *I.R.E. Trans. PGIT*, **4** (March 1958), 4–14.

79. Fortet, R. and Blanc-LaPierre, A., *Théorie des Fonctions Aléatoires.* Paris: Masson et Cie., 1953. Chapter VII.

80. Deutsch, R., "Piecewise Quadratic Detector," *I.R.E. Convention Record,* **Pt. 4** (1956), 15.

81. Deutsch, R., "On the Distribution of Nonlinear Circuit Transformations of a Markov Process," *Proceedings of the Symposium on Nonlinear Circuit Analysis,* Polytechnic Institute of Brooklyn, New York, VI (1956), 243–253.

82. Kamke, E., *Differential Gleichungen, Lösungsmethoden und Lösungen.* New York: Chelsea Publishing Co., 1948.

83. Dressel, F. G., "The Fundamental Solution of the Parabolic Equation," *Duke Mathematical Journal,* 1940, 186.

84. Kopi Husimi, "Miscellanea in Elementary Quantum Mechanics, II," *Progress of Theoretical Physics,* **9** (April 1953), 381–402.

85. Dr. Worthie Doyle, in a private communication, pointed out an error in reference 81, and was kind enough to furnish a corrected solution which was incorporated into Sec. 7.6, example a.

86. Jagerman, D. L. and Fogel, L. J., "Some General Aspects of the Sampling Theorem," *I.R.E. Trans. PGIT,* **IT-2,** No. 4 (December 1956), 139–146.

87. Whittaker, J. M., *Interpolatory Function Theory,* Cambridge Tracts in Mathematics and Mathematical Physics, **No. 33.** London: Cambridge University Press, 1955.

88. Nörlund, N. E., "Sur les Formules d'Interpretation de Stirling et Newton," *Annales Science de l'Ecole Normale,* **39** (1922), 343-403; **40** (1923) 35-54.

89. Weiss, P., "Sampling Theorems Associated with Sturm-Liouville Systems," (Abstract 459) *Bulletin of the American Mathematical Society,* **63** (1957).

90. Kramer, H. P., "A Generalized Sampling Theorem," *Journal of Mathematics and Physics,* **38** (April 1959), 68–72.

91. Lloyd, S. P., "A Sampling Theorem for Stationary (Wide Sense) Stochastic Processes," *Transactions of the American Mathematical Society*, **92** (July 1959), 1–12.

92. Balakrishnan, A. V., "A Note on the Sampling Principle for Continuous Signals," *I.R.E. Trans. PGIT*, **IT-3,** No. 2 (June 1957), 143–146.

93. Titchmarsh, E. C., *Theory of Functions.* Oxford, England: Oxford University Press, 1950.

94. Bennett, W. R., "Spectra of Quantized Signals," *Bell System Technical Journal*, **27** (July 1948), 446–472.

95. Max, J., "Quantizing for Minimum Distortion," *I.R.E. Trans. PGIT*, **IT-6,** No. 1 (March 1960), 7.

INDEX

Auxiliary R function, 116
Average (*see* Expected value)
  temporal, 71

Backward equation, 120
Bandwidth limited, 9
Bessel function, 142
  modified, 142
Beta function, 144
Binomial expansion, 142
Biorthogonal, 76
Bromwich path, 14

Cardinal series, 130
Center frequency, 56
Chapman-Kolmogorov equation, 117
Characteristic function, 116
  correlation function relation, 14
  filtered thermal noise, 55
  joint, 17
  joint Gausian, 21, 69
  moment generating property, 34
  square law device, 48, 53
Characteristic function method
  error function, 24
  fundamental equation, 14
  ideal limiter, 21
  linear detector, 23
  square law detector, 67
Continuity condition, 46
Convergence in mean, 47
Correlation function, 100
  as time series, 7
  cross-covariance, 5
  envelope, 70
  Hilbert transform, 6
  input, 16
  output, 21
  normalized, 31
Correlation function (*Cont.*)
  series expansion, 82
  spectrum, 6
Cumulants, 51

Determining equation, 118
Distribution function (*see* Frequency function)
  Schwartz, 110
Decorrelation function, 31
Detector
  envelope square law, 30
  generic, 62
  linear, 23, 64
  moments, output, 44
  square-law, 67
  zero frequency terms, 63

Eigenfunctions, 46, 48, 52, 93, 132
Eigenvalues, 46, 52, 93, 132
Elliptic integrals
  complete, 30
  complete, first kind, 143
  complete, second kind, 143
Envelope
  notion, 1
  pre-envelope, 3
  sine wave plus noise, 10
Envelope function, 1
  averaged squared, 7
  random process, 2
  real-time series, 3
  relative, 41
Error function, 24, 142
  Price method, 25
Expected value, 5 (*see also* Average)
Exponential function, 142

Factorial function, 22, 32, 139

Filter, impulse response, 36
Fokker-Planck equation, 118
Forward equation, 117
Fourier coefficients, 47
Frequency
  midband, 2
  positive, 5
Frequency function (*see also* Probability density)
  class F, 89
  filter, 9
  joint amplitude, Gaussian, 12
  joint correlated, 18
  joint Gaussian, 16, 20, 43, 59, 94
  Poisson, 34
  Rayleigh, 32
  representation, moments, 109
  second order, 88
  sine wave plus noise, 44
  transition probability, 116
  transform, joint characteristic, 27
Functional
  class $L_2(C)$, 107
  random process, 112

Gamma function, incomplete, 142
Gating function, 126
Gaussian process, product, 42
Gottlieb polynomials, 143
Gram-Charlier
  pulse shape, 86
  series, 76
Green's function, 55, 124

Hermite polynomial, 45, 76, 94, 142
  addition formula, 87
  normalized, 106
  n-variate, 107
Hermitian symmetric, 46
Hypergeometric function, 22, 139
  confluent, 45
  generalized, 140

Ideal limiter, 25
Impedance weighting function, 104
Integral equation
  homogeneous, 46
  linear homogeneous, 93
  random process, 115
Interpolation error, 129

Jacobi polynomials, 142

Kernel
  homogeneous integral equation, 56
  n- iterated, 53

Lagrange
  coefficients, 128
  interpolation polynomial, 128
Laguerre polynomials, 142
  generalized, 79, 142
Laplace transform, 14
Legendre polynomials, 143
Limiter, ideal, 21
Linear filter, 8, 55
  orthogonal, 83

Markov process, 116, 118
Mehler's expansion, 109
Mercer's theorem, 46
Modified Bessel function, 11
Modulation, 1
  indices, 72
  random process, 71
Modulator, 62, 63
Moments, 120
  first order, 76
  first order envelope, 44
  fourth order Gaussian, 36
  generating function, 34
  n'th order, 27
  output, power law, 44
  representation, frequency function, 109
  standard, 45, 77
Multiplier, 63

Non-Gaussian process, 26, 40, 80
Non-linear
  class F, 105
  device, 95
  noise problem, 114
  operator, 105
Normalized process, 20
Nyquist interval, 58, 128

Orthogonal
  random variable, 46
  representation, 105
Orthonormal polynomial
  determination, frequency function, 89

Piece-wise function, 21
Piece-wise quadratic, 119
Poisson distribution, 34
Power density function
  cross-covariance, 6
  cross-power, 5
Power law device, 44
Pre-envelope, linear filter, 9
Price method
  error function, 25
  ideal limiter, 22
  linear detector, 23
Probability density (*see also* Frequency function)
  joint Gaussian, 10
  sine wave plus noise, 10

Q-polynomials, 80
Quantized process
  equal steps, 135
  unequal steps, 137

R-function, 116
Random process
  bandwidth limited, 127
  complex representation, 126
  ergodic, 5
  Markov, 116, 118
  orthogonal, 46
  quasi-stationary, 71
  series representation, 2
  Uhlenbeck-Ornstein, 118
  uncorrelated, 6
  Wiener-Lévy, 115, 118
  White-Gaussian, 106
Rayleigh distribution, 32
Rectifier, half-way, 64
Reduced equation, 118
Residue, 23, 68
Ricatti equation, 119

Sampling function, 126
Series
  bilinear, 56
  Gram-Charlier, 76
  random process, representation, 47
Signal-to-noise ratio, 59
Solution, closed form, 26
Sonine polynomial, 142
Spectral density, 114
Spectral function, 9
Spectral limited, 9
Square law device, 47
Squarer, 52
Stationary, wide sense, 46
Struve's function, 143
System kernel, 52

Theorem
  Mercer, 46
  Price, 16
  transform, 36
Transform
  Fourier, 3
  Hilbert, 3
  pre-envelope, 4
  theorem, 36

Ultraspherical polynomials, 143

Volterra expansion, 105
Volterra reciprocal function, 49
Variance, 33

Wiener process, 115, 118, 121
Whittaker's function, 142

Zero-memory, 57
  device, 16
  transformation, 90